WILLIAM K. WIDGER, JR.
2800 BYRON STREET
SILVER SPRING, MARYLAND

AMERICA ON THE MOON

AMERICA ON THE MOON:

THE ENTERPRISE OF THE SIXTIES

By JAY HOLMES

Preface by E. C. Welsh, Executive Secretary
National Aeronautics and Space Council

J. B. LIPPINCOTT COMPANY
PHILADELPHIA AND NEW YORK

PREFACE

In undertaking this book, the author made two impressively sound decisions. He chose a most dynamic and exciting subject, and he recognized the urgent need for a fuller public understanding of the significance of space exploration and of space technology.

Mr. Holmes focuses the major attention of his research on the most ambitious endeavor in the history of mankind, i.e., the effort to transport men safely to the moon and back to earth. For a moon trip, there is specific requirement for powerful rockets, sophisticated spacecraft, trained and carefully selected astronauts and protection against the multiple hazards of a hostile environment. Any nation which can successfully master this objective can do many other things which can either threaten or protect the world's security and which can improve to an immeasurable degree the conditions of life here on earth.

We are in a space race with the Soviet Union. The prize at stake is survival as a free nation. In view of the Soviet threat, we have no choice except to compete in this race and compete to win.

We must win the space race unless we want to become a second-rate nation in technology, in science and in world influence. More important still, the outcome of this race may well determine whether or not freedom becomes a second-rate commodity. Moreover, the values received from our efforts in space will eventually exceed the costs many times over. Such returns from the space effort will be reflected in education, in medicine,

in metallurgy, in international prestige, in diplomatic negotiations, in defense against aggression and in higher standards of
living generally. We in the United States can accomplish all of
those things with an annual expenditure averaging perhaps one
per cent of our gross national product.

The National Aeronautics and Space Act of 1958 states that
it is the policy of the United States that "activities in space
should be devoted to peaceful purposes for the benefit of all
mankind." That is a sound policy for any vigorous, peace-loving
nation. However, it should be clear that we do not have a division between peaceful and non-peaceful objectives for space.
Rather, we have space missions to help keep the peace, and space
missions to improve our ability to live well in peace.

The author tells what this country is doing and what it is
planning in the broad field of space. As a responsible and qualified writer, he has translated the complexities of space exploration into readable and understandable language, interspersing
throughout relevant items of historical interest along with ref-
erences to the most current of our space projects. His views of
the facts are, of course, his own, but he has made an energetic
effort to get at the facts prior to the development of his opinions.
That is both noteworthy and commendable. However, even if
the author had given what I would consider the appropriate
amount of attention to the activities of the National Aeronautics
and Space Council during 1961, I would still neither indicate
agreement nor express disagreement with his observations or
conclusions. Each reader, and the book warrants many, must
make his own judgment regarding the author's views and per-
spective.

E. C. Welsh
Executive Secretary
National Aeronautics and Space Council

FOREWORD

This book seeks to give a broad picture of the why and the how of American activities in space, with emphasis on the civilian portion. It is impossible to discuss any scientific project without going into some technical detail, but I have tried to keep the discussion at a level that can be understood by any intelligent person, regardless of whether he has studied science.

I have also tried to be authentic. Misinformation has become mixed with facts in much that has been published about space in recent years. Real projects have become confused with mere proposals. Serious proposals are mixed up with "blue sky" ideas. And blue sky ideas are sometimes mistaken for science fiction. There is a whole spectrum that runs from the real and probable to the fantastic and impossible. I have taken the position that the real is strange enough to astound us. This book is focused on real projects, now under way, and proposals that are under serious consideration by the U.S. government.

In my efforts to achieve reality, I have had valuable help from hundreds of people with administrative and technical responsibility in many government agencies, private laboratories and industrial concerns active in the space effort. Administrator James E. Webb of the National Aeronautics and Space Administration has provided both official assistance and personal encouragement without which this project would have been impossible. Other government agencies that have been helpful include the National Aeronautics and Space Council, the Department of Defense, the Weather Bureau, the Federal Communications Commission, the Atomic Energy Commission and three Congressional committees, the Joint Committee on Atomic Energy, the Senate Committee on Aeronautical and Space Sciences and the House Committee on Science and Astronautics. It would not be feasible to list the hundreds of persons in these agencies and elsewhere who provided information. But I do want to acknowledge the help of those who have read one or more chapters of the manuscript and have made valuable suggestions. They include Administrator Webb, Executive Secretary Edward C. Welsh of the National Aeronautics and Space Council, General Bernard A. Schriever, Director Wernher von Braun of the NASA Marshall Space Flight Center, Vice Admiral John T. Hayward, Ambassador James J. Wadsworth, Chief Francis W. Reichelderfer of the Weather Bureau, Federal Communications Commissioner T. A. M. Craven, Chief David S. Johnson of the Weather Bureau's Meteorological Satellite Laboratory, physicist S. Fred Singer, economist Otto R. Reischer, disarmament specialist Paul Auerswald, military expert William Leavitt and the following members of the NASA staff: Richard J. H. Barnes, Richard B. Canright, Paul J. Coleman Jr., John H. Disher, Harold B. Finger, Foster Haley, Eldon W. Hall, Capt. Richard J. Hayes, Abraham Hyatt, Fred D. Kochendorfer, Elliot Mitchell, Homer E. Newell, Robert G. Nunn Jr., Franklyn Phillips, Col. Robert E. Warren, William K. Widger Jr. and Richard E. Wright. (It will be apparent from the above listing that I have used no title with the names of doctors of philosophy. I have followed that practice throughout the book for the purpose of brevity.)

In most cases, I have followed the suggestions made by those consulted. But on a few controversial matters, I have had to reach my own conclusions, for which no one else should be held responsible. Furthermore, it has not been practical to ask each person to comment on every chapter on which he might be qualified to express an opinion. My views are of course unofficial, since, as a private citizen, I have had no access to classified information.

I could not have understood a good deal of the material in this book, much less have written it, had I not spent the academic year 1958-59 as a fellow in the Advanced Science Writing Program of the Graduate School of Journalism, Columbia University. The fellowship was made possible by a grant provided by the Sloan and Rockefeller Foundations.

Pat Frank urged me to start this book. F. Clarke Newlon, Joseph A. Stein, Paul P. Haney and Richard T. Mittauer provided valuable help in the early stages. Later, I was fortunate to have constant encouragement and advice from Emery C. Wine. Bacil Guiley and Joseph Phillips drew the diagrams. The title was suggested by Peter Andrews. James R. Aswell and Alan Berg made useful suggestions on style.

Finally, my wife, Beatrice, edited every page of the manuscript, assisted in many revisions and was my final authority on whether the material was understandable to nontechnical readers.

Jay Holmes

October 16, 1961

TABLE OF CONTENTS

APPENDICES

I believe this nation should commit itself to achieving the goal, before this decade is out, of landing a man on the moon and returning him safely to earth. No single space project in this period will be more exciting, or more important for the long-range exploration of space; and none will be so difficult or expensive to accomplish. . . . We propose to accelerate development of the appropriate lunar space craft. We propose to develop alternate liquid and solid fuel boosters of much larger size than any now being developed, until certain which is superior. We propose additional funds for other engine development and for unmanned explorations—explorations which are particularly important for one purpose which this nation will never overlook: the survival of the man who first makes this daring flight. But in a real sense, it will not be one man going to the moon—it will be an entire nation. For all of us must work to put him there.

John F. Kennedy, May 25, 1961

SECTION

I QUESTIONS

1. WHY?

WHEN HISTORY finally assesses the twentieth century, two scientific achievements will outrank all the wars, revolutions and depressions. One will be the use of nuclear energy, made possible by Albert Einstein's theories of relativity. The other will will be man's escape from the planet that gave him birth.

For thousands and perhaps millions of years to come, school children will have to memorize a date in the latter 1960s—probably during the second administration of John F. Kennedy—the day men first set foot on the moon.

Who will they be? Possibly Russians. The crew may include Yuri Gagarin and Gherman Titov, the first men in orbit about the earth. Conceivably western Europeans. The Common Market is wealthy enough to send a space ship to the moon. But if U.S. government plans reach fruition, the first crew will consist of three Americans—two pilot astronauts and a scientist. The astronauts are already in training. By the time this book appears, one may have flown around the earth in a Project Mercury capsule. The process of choosing the scientist has not even begun, however. He may now be taking magnetic readings at the South Pole, measuring infrared radiation near a volcano in Hawaii or observing the aurora in Alaska.

Like Columbus' arrival at San Salvador, the first lunar landing will be remembered in history as a symbol of civilization bursting through a barrier. It will also mark the beginning of a new age of exploration, whose end we cannot foresee. But unlike the navigators of the fifteenth and sixteenth centuries, explorers of our time are not entrepreneurs who raise money, outfit ships and hire crews on their own initiative. The cost of flying beyond the earth is so vast that no individual, no private company or foundation and only a few governments can afford to sponsor it. Whole nations must take part in the adventure.

Why fly to the moon? For the explorer, the reasons are simple. A scientist, he seeks knowledge. An adventurer, he seeks new experience, the thrill of conquering a hostile environment. An ambitious man, he seeks glory, a place in history.

But why should American taxpayers underwrite so expensive an enterprise? Some of the reasons are the same as the explorer's. We too seek knowledge. We are curious to know what is up there. The whole nation shares the thrill of the adventure. Not only the explorers but their country is glorified by the achievement. Twenty-five years ago, Franklin D. Roosevelt told a generation of Americans it had a rendezvous with destiny. This generation has a rendezvous with the cosmos.

There are practical reasons as well. To reach the moon, it will be necessary to develop new technology, which will improve living standards on earth, enable American industry to compete in world markets and increase our total national strength. Development of automation, computers, energy conversion, low temperature techniques, systems engineering, life sciences, new fuels, better materials and improved communications are examples of scientific and technological advances that must be speeded to fulfill the requirements of this vast project. The new technology will feed back directly into our everyday life, enabling industry to produce better goods in greater quantity at less cost. Some of the new products have already begun to flow into the civilian economy. Better-tasting orange juice and long-term storage of blood are now available because industry has learned to work with the low temperatures of liquid oxygen and nitrogen. Crockery that can go from the freezer directly to the oven is made from a material developed for missile radomes. Use of sunlight to develop power for satellites is making electricity available for homes in remote areas of the earth. But it is just beginning. "We have barely touched the economic potential of this era of new energy sources and expanding frontiers in physical chemistry, solid-state physics, polymer chemistry and the design of electronic equipment," says Secretary of Commerce Luther H. Hodges.

Our population is growing rapidly. Our productive capacity

must grow even more rapidly if we are to continue to improve our standard of living. Only new technology can make the expansion possible. On the world scale, the situation is growing desperate. As disease is checked and death rates fall in underdeveloped countries, the population explodes. Extremely rapid economic growth is necessary just to stand still. To be assured of the technological progress that will enable us to provide for the world's children and grandchildren, we must push back all the frontiers of science and technology as speedily as possible—on the earth, under the earth, in the sea, in the air and in outer space. We don't know which will provide the breakthroughs, the big payoffs. We must cover all bets.

In itself, flying to the moon may not solve earthly problems. But a long time ago, a great teacher told men they do not live by bread alone. Flight to the moon is also a symbol of what science can achieve—that man, a little, insignificant two-legged creature, with just his brain and his hands, now can bend a universe to his will. It demonstrates that nothing is impossible, if we simply make up our minds to do it. It sets a goal that spurs the advance of science and technology on a broad scale. It develops a sense of urgency in the search for knowledge. It dramatizes science, so that young people are willing to take it up as a career and elderly legislators are willing to vote funds for research and education. It is an inspiration to the nation, creating a sense of dedication and unity.

Some of President Kennedy's advisers believe the expedition to the moon ought to be an international project. The moon is visible from every spot on earth. It belongs equally to the three billion human inhabitants of this planet. A joint endeavor to explore our common property could help break down barriers of hate and suspicion that divide the nations.

But an international endeavor seems to be out of the question, at least in the present climate of international affairs. As is pointed out by Mtislav Keldysh, president of the Soviet Academy of Sciences, "Carrier rockets are not only instruments of peace." Since rockets are war instruments, a nation that has superior rockets guards its secrets carefully, the Soviet government evidently believes. There seems to be little prospect of agreement on a joint project, at least until the time when American rockets are demonstrably equal to those of the Soviets.

And so America must go it alone on this greatest peaceful enterprise of human history. "We must push on with all determination into space," says Vice President Lyndon B. Johnson, "so as to win it for peace before some other nation conquers it for war and destruction." Says James E. Webb, U.S. space administrator, "You cannot afford to fall backward from what you are capable of doing in science and technology without finding that you have realized less than your potential, and frequently that someone has passed you by."

In President Kennedy's view, "We cannot possibly permit any country whose intentions toward us may be hostile to dominate space." But we seek no military bases on the moon. U.S. and Soviet scientists have already agreed that the moon should be international, like Antarctica. In time, the two governments seem certain to agree with their eminent citizens. After battling the lunar environment, the explorers will be too exhausted to fight one another. The stringent weight limitations aboard a moon ship will allow no room for guns. But while accomplishing the flight to the moon and back, the nation will develop a whole series of capabilities that will prove valuable in military ways until the day of total disarmament. "All the mechanics of operation involved in a lunar landing and return—propulsion, guidance, rendezvous, controlled landing—are vital to the U.S. military posture," says General Bernard A. Schriever.

The basic technology also will make possible a whole series of applications of combined civil, military and scientific importance. In a few years, the use of satellites will vastly expand the radio channels for communication around the world, making possible global television, cheaper international telephone and telegraph service and instantaneous transmission of great quantities of information. A satellite system will revolutionize the art of weather prediction, advance weather research and possibly enable science to make a beginning at controlling the weather. Satellites will help ships find their way at sea when the stars are obscured by clouds. With satellites, it will be possible to map the earth exactly and to learn more about its shape and the composition of the interior.

Escape through the earth's atmosphere will open wide new vistas in astronomy. For the first time, science will see the stars in their true colors, in the ultraviolet, infrared and X-ray wavelengths, and without the blurs in the picture caused by an atmosphere that acts like a greasy thumbprint on the lens of every telescope. On the moon, geologists will be able to examine land unaffected by weather, erosion and mountain-building processes for four billion years, from which they expect to learn the secrets of the birth of the solar system. Biologists expect the search for primitive life on the moon to yield the secret of how life began on earth, and whether it is distributed widely in the universe.

But the inspirational, practical, scientific and possible military reasons still do not add up to the total justification of America's sponsorship of this enormous undertaking. A final ingredient is the long struggle between East and West for world leadership. Everything we do in this country, in Southern schools, in manufacturing goods for world markets, in Hollywood movies, in the armed services and the civilian branches of government, in our treatment of foreign visitors plays a part in the contest to determine which form of government shall prevail. "The great battleground for the defense and expansion of freedom today is the whole southern half of the globe," says President Kennedy. These peoples still have not made their final choice between communism and democracy. They will judge the opposing systems in part by what they see and learn of their accomplishments.

For a long time, the world judged the United States and Europe, the advanced Western nations, as world leaders in technology. Now, however, the judgment is uncertain. By exploding nuclear and thermonuclear bombs in the late 1940s and early 1950s, Soviet Russia began chipping away at the notion. In 1957, the idea of Russian technological progress broke through. In August, 1957, the Soviet Union announced the successful testing of an intercontinental ballistic missile. And on October 4, 1957, a Friday night that will rank in psychological impact with a Sunday morning in December, 1941, Russia launched the first satellite into orbit around the earth.

Sputnik, the most successful advertising stunt in history, ended forever the idea that Soviet Russia is a backward nation, unable to compete with the West technologically. The satellite circled the globe every ninety-six minutes. It was visible to the naked eye at sunrise and sunset. Its beeping signal could be heard by amateur radio operators the world over. It provided evidence more convincing than millions of words of propaganda that the Communist system was succeeding.

Two months later, on December 6, 1957, the world saw another symbol. The ignominious failure of the first Vanguard seemed to be a sign of American decadence, a stage in the decline of Western civilization.

Within a few months, however, America did manage to launch satellites. Fifteen months after the Soviet ICBM flight, the American Atlas did the same. In the years that followed, American mass-production methods made it possible to produce more ICBMs than the Soviet Union and to launch three times as many satellites. And American science and industry developed the most telling weapon of all, the nuclear-powered Polaris submarine, which could lie quietly at the bottom of the ocean for months at a time, ready to fire sixteen missiles with thermonuclear warheads on a few minutes notice. To this day, Soviet Russia has nothing to match Polaris.

Spectacular achievements in space, however, enabled Soviet Russia to maintain an appearance of superior power, advancing technology and a growing economy. In fact, the total destructive power of U.S. bombers, ICBMs, Polaris submarines and intermediate-range missiles on allied bases is far greater than that of the Soviet Union. There has never been a day when U.S. strategic power was not superior. No such day will come in the foreseeable future. In fact, the United States is advancing the frontiers of technology—nuclear energy, solar power, computers, polymer chemistry and others—more rapidly than the Soviet Union, although a spirited competition is in progress in some areas. In fact, the Soviet standard of living is appalling. Millions of families live in single rooms. Industrial production is well behind that of the United States. The food shortage is chronic. The Soviet Union has far to go before it can talk realistically of catching up with the United States.

But appearances often count for more than facts. In the first four years of the Space Age, the historic milestones were Soviet accomplishments—the launching of Sputnik, hitting the moon September 13, 1959, orbiting of the first man April 12, 1961. "A nation's prestige is now measured by a new yardstick," Vice-President Johnson points out, "its achievements, or lack thereof, in space."

In the summer of 1961, Khrushchev wrung the utmost in prestige from the Soviet space achievements. After the orbital flights of Yuri Gagarin and Gherman Titov had demonstrated the effectiveness of the big Soviet space rocket, Khrushchev cast about for a military application. The same rocket that carries a five-ton spacecraft into orbit can probably launch a payload weighing at least ten tons on an ICBM trajectory. And so Khrushchev announced plans to develop a monster bomb with the explosive yield of 100 million tons (megatons) of TNT, 5000 times as powerful as the bomb dropped on Hiroshima.

From the military viewpoint, such a bomb is terribly wasteful. Much of its energy is expended creating a hole in the ground and making a loud noise. More damage can be done with ten bombs a tenth as large; more yet with 100 bombs of one megaton yield. But a monster bomb has one great advantage for the Soviets. It frightens people. Although it is militarily wasteful, its mighty blast has telling impact on the minds of people in neutral countries.

The United States of America, which came into existence proclaiming a decent respect for the opinions of mankind, cannot adopt such tactics. We could not conduct operations whose only purpose is to terrorize smaller, weaker nations. Nevertheless, we too must consider national prestige. It is an essential part of our justification for spending billions of dollars in space.

We must conduct a program that emphasizes where we are strong, where we are superior to the Soviet Union. We must pursue aggressive space science research, not only because of the knowledge to be gained, but because it demonstrates the strength of American science. We must vigorously develop weather and communication satellite systems, not only because of their intrinsic value, but because they show how the American system produces things of practical use. We must press forward with the nuclear rocket and nuclear space power sources, not only because they may make it possible to explore the ends of the solar system, but because they remind the world that the use of atomic energy is an American invention, in which we are far ahead of the Soviets.

But America's greatest asset in the battle for men's minds is not a technical skill. It is our open society. It is our willingness to invite the world to watch, not knowing in advance whether the experiment will succeed or fail. It is our willingness to share the scientific results of our investigations—not just a selected few, but all of them. It is our willingness to invite other nations to share in the practical benefits, now and not on some hypothetical future day when total disarmament arrives and all international tensions have disappeared.

The world is tired and numbed by propaganda. Yuri Gagarin's flight around the world, a historic achievement, lost some of its impact because the details were obscured. No independent observers watched as he left or when he returned. Soviet propaganda quoted him as making statements that he sang a patriotic song when he landed, that he recognized collective farms from space. The sense of adventure is lost when the accomplishment is announced only if it succeeds. The world cheered just as loudly for Alan Shepard three weeks later when he flew a mere 300 miles; America had invited the world to share the experience. We shall not always be as successful as on May 5, 1961. Tragedy may even occur. But our willingness to carry out our business in the open will be a powerful factor in the contest for prestige.

The Shepard flight accomplished so much for the United States in world opinion that the Soviets felt forced to relax their policy of secrecy. Soviet correspondents were permitted to observe and report a major rocket launching for the first time on August 6, 1961, for the flight of Gherman Titov. No foreigners were allowed, but afterward President Keldysh of the Soviet Academy of Sciences promised that, too, would take place in the future.

We cannot claim world leadership, however, if we compete only in areas where we are already strong, in science, practical applications, nuclear energy and the willingness to operate openly. We must strive to make up the deficits as well. We must carry out a program that in as short a period as possible will convince the world that we are leaders in every phase of the competition. It is time, says President Kennedy, "for this nation to take a clearly leading role in space achievement."

But which goal to adopt? After orbiting a single man in Project Mercury, the next major milestone of the American program will be the orbital flight of three men, possibly by early 1964, in Project Apollo. But there seems to be little doubt that Russia can accomplish such a flight sooner. Thus it would be foolish to set that as a major national objective. After that will come the flight around the moon, which we may be able to accomplish by 1965 or 1966. Again, Russia will have an advantage, although if we press hard—and are lucky—we may have an outside chance to do it first. But again, it is not wise to establish an event in which our chances are marginal as the most important.

Fortunately, however, there is one event which will be recognized by the world as historic, which can take place in this decade and which America has a good chance to perform first. Landing men on the moon and bringing them back safely is so stupendous an undertaking that carrying it out will take up a sizable fraction of either nation's wealth. The total potential of the two economies is involved. The cost will be at least twenty billion dollars. If the landing is not carried out as soon as expected, the cost may rise to thirty billions, perhaps even forty. The length of time involved—six years at the bare minimum from the time it was authorized by Congress in 1961—means that the Russian lead in rocket development is not a decisive advantage. There is time for American science, productive capacity and natural and human resources to close the gap and forge into the lead. "When it comes to all the technology required," says Space Administrator James E. Webb, "I think we're starting slightly ahead."

However, the idea of a race bothers many American scientists. They are willing to approve the objective of manned flight to the moon, although they doubt that the expenditure can be justified on purely scientific grounds. They are willing to concede that inspiration, practical applications, national prestige and possible military benefits may also be important reasons. They find it particularly undignified, however, for two great nations to pour out their treasure in a pell-mell race.

But the East-West competition has existed for years; it began long before space flight became possible. The race for the moon is only the latest and most dramatic stage of the contest, which will probably endure long after the moon is dotted with scientific stations of many nations. "This is a contest of nerve and will," President Kennedy has declared. "The next ten, fifteen or twenty years may determine the outcome. The Soviet system and our system are on trial. The question will be which system has the longest staying power—which can maintain itself in good times and bad."

During the long struggle, America will encounter defeats as well as victories. They will require of us something we find very difficult—self-restraint in the face of adversity. Americans are wonderfully magnanimous when we are on top, but we are poor

losers. The bloody nose we received in Cuba in 1961 created
pressures for action that would have been very foolish. Later
that year, Khrushchev's brinkmanship set in motion public demands that we drop hydrogen bombs. We have no experience,
no skill in finishing second at anything, even temporarily. After
Gagarin's orbital flight, Pierre Mendes-France, former French
Premier, remarked of the American people, "They now know
how far behind they are and a great people with a highly developed taste for competition and championship finds this most
painful."

Space flight is a peaceful form of competition in which we
can release our hostile feelings. Alan Shepard's success, coming
right after Cuba, diverted the public pressure for action there.
It may be undignified to race into space, but it is a constructive
activity. And in itself, there is nothing wrong with competition.
It brings out the best in people, institutions, private companies
and branches of government. Why should it not do the same
for whole nations?

And the race for the moon is a competition America can win.

2. HOW?

BEFORE A MANNED FLIGHT can be launched to the moon, thousands of specific tasks must be accomplished. They include choosing locations, building facilities, developing and testing rockets, spacecraft and ground equipment, hiring personnel, selecting contractors, monitoring their work and flying a long series of preparatory and training missions. It is possible to predict with fairly high accuracy how long the individual tasks will take. But in research and development projects, it is not possible to predict with any great assurance the accomplishment of the whole mission.

Despite the uncertainty, a target date—January, 1967—has been set for landing an American expedition on the moon. The date was established so that the program can be organized and future plans laid out. Any major activity of the U.S. government must be planned a long time in advance. The fiscal year runs from July 1 to June 30. If a government agency is to spend money on July 1, the appropriation bill will have to be approved by Congress and signed by the President before that date. But the detailed planning within the government agency and the Bureau of the Budget must begin more than a year before Congress acts. For rocket projects, the situation is complicated by the problem of "lead time," which is simply the delay between time of decision and time of fruition. Everything involved takes a long time to accomplish—the bigger the rocket, the longer the lead time. Before the work can even begin, months and perhaps years are required for the planning, design and

[27

construction of testing and launching facilities. And if the facilities are constructed concurrently with the work on the rocket itself, the intervening research often uncovers reasons for important changes in design after the foundation has been laid and the cement poured, making it necessary to do much of the facility work over again. Nevertheless, many important tasks must be done concurrently to save time, even though the cost is higher in the end. It is a question of judgment, both of the responsible executives and of Congress, how much money should be spent to buy time.

In concurrent development, an engineering team is given the assignment to build a part or system without knowing the exact nature of the adjoining parts and systems. Even with the greatest care, the pieces may not fit perfectly together the first time round. This so-called "interface" problem is not merely technical. All of the work is done by people, who have likes and dislikes, foibles and weaknesses, biases and prejudices. The most able people, in engineering as in other walks of life, have blind spots in their vision. An otherwise brilliant scientist or engineer may take a simple, incontrovertible statement of fact as a personal affront; motives often become inextricably bound up in technical decisions. Sometimes the most difficult engineering task is to get the people involved to fit together.

Many missile and space engineers believe that the largest factor for delay in U.S. missile and space programs is in decision making. Often, they believe, a wrong decision is better than a delayed decision. For example, it may turn out that two ways of building a piece of equipment are almost equal. Let us say that two months can be saved by choosing Method A. But even if Method B is chosen, the delay need not be serious. If the decision is made promptly, work can begin two months earlier.

However, meeting the schedule is uncertain even if decisions are made on time. Space Administrator James E. Webb says there are 2200 jobs that must be performed to land men on the moon safely. Let us suppose that each is carried out in a way that insures 99.9 per cent success—only one chance in 1000 of delay. Nevertheless, the laws of probability tell us two sad facts. First, the chances are that two or three of the 2200 tasks will encounter delay. Second, there is only one chance in ten that all will be done on time.

In fact, it isn't possible to lay out plans that will assure 99.9

per cent certainty for each of the 2200 tasks. Some are in the area of the unknown. The engineers cannot say yet how they can be done. None is believed to be impossible. But some of them present severe technical problems that must be solved. Some of the estimates of the time required are simply educated guesswork. Thus the probability is considerably less than one in ten that the American explorers will step onto the moon's surface in January, 1967. A landing any time during that year will be counted as a remarkable success—particularly if they arrive ahead of their Soviet competitors.

Nevertheless, such a schedule must be established. The over-all timetable must be broken down into thousands of interim dates for accomplishment of preliminary tasks. The schedule is a statement of requirements for their accomplishment—delivery of parts and supplies, for example. It is not a promise that an experiment will be performed by a given date.

With the best of intentions it is almost impossible to make some decisions early without taking a grave risk of being wrong. Because of the lead time involved, a decision was needed in 1961 on whether to use liquid or solid fuels for the big first and second stages of the lunar rocket. Solid fuels appeared promising, but no one in a responsible position felt there was enough technical information and experience available to justify gambling on them. Liquid-fueled rockets would probably cost more and take longer to develop, but there was more experience and data to rely upon. To avoid making a wrong decision so early in the program, President Kennedy recommended and the Congress approved parallel programs to develop both solid and liquid-fueled rockets. Both will be carried along for a few years until enough technical information is available to determine which is superior for the job. The cost is obviously higher when parallel programs are carried out. But the additional money buys assurance that the job will be done at the earliest possible date.

A similar decision faces the nation in 1962. No one can say at present whether direct ascent or rendezvous in space will provide the most effective means of reaching the moon. Just as between liquid and solid fuels, the choice is between a brute-force approach that will be expensive and time-consuming but certain as against a risky, new method that may save both time and money.

Direct ascent involves building a huge rocket, the Nova, whose thrust on takeoff would be at least 12,000,000 pounds—eight times as great as the Saturn C-1, which is now undergoing early flight tests. Nova would be about 350 feet tall and would require a launching tower almost half the size of the Empire State Building—and movable. Building, developing and testing so huge a rocket is bound to take many years.

By use of rendezvous in space, many U.S. rocket specialists believe time can be saved by using smaller rockets than the Nova, firing them in quantity and assembling the parts in space. Such a process would take maximum advantage of America's talent for mass production and thus might be cheaper in the end. But rendezvous is a gamble because no one has any experience to draw upon. It is impossible to predict what difficulties may develop. There is no possibility of carrying out even a demonstration of rendezvous with rockets and spacecraft available in 1962, when the decision must be made on priority.

But if the American people are willing to spend enough money, it would be possible to carry on parallel direct-ascent and rendezvous development programs at top priority until such time as it is reasonable to make a choice. The first manned rendezvous experiments can probably be carried out by 1964. Presumably, the decision could be made by then.

There is still another possible method of reducing the size of the lunar landing rocket—the use of a nuclear-propelled upper stage. The flight test of the nuclear rocket, however, cannot come before 1965. By that time, presumably, one of the other two methods will have been proved out. But if trouble develops with both rendezvous and direct ascent by chemical rocket propulsion, and if the nuclear rocket flight succeeds, it will be available to fill the breach.

Fortunately, no additional money need be spent to assure that nuclear propulsion will be available. The United States plans to push along its nuclear rocket development (Project Rover) even if it is not available for the first landing on the moon. Nuclear propulsion is expected to provide a vital element in the transportation system in support of the lunar base. In addition, in the next decade nuclear propulsion will provide the means for manned exploration of the planets.

Both rendezvous and the nuclear upper stage can make use of a rocket about half the size of Nova, whose first stage would be a cluster of four or five engines, each with about the same total power as the current version of Saturn. Developing such a rocket will enable America to bet on not one but two promising methods of saving the time required to build the big Nova.

I have dwelt at length on the problem of propulsion because of its immediacy. Large rockets take so long to build that the major decisions have to be made very early in the program. Rockets are the biggest expense item as well. The primary questions about rockets are really questions of how much money to spend—which raise in turn the question of how important it is to America to win this race. If we want to go all-out, we should carry on parallel programs that will cost more than is now contemplated. On the other hand, if even the presently planned cost seems too great, we can carry out the program on a much more limited basis by cutting out one of the rocket programs, and settling on liquid or solid propulsion immediately. That decision would save money, but it would greatly reduce the likelihood that American astronauts will be first on the moon. Such a decision is one for the whole American people.

After the propulsion problem is settled, many difficult technical questions will remain. Spacecraft must be designed that will pack equipment, food, water, air and supplies to support three men for several weeks into a volume about as large as a station wagon. Means must be developed for guiding and controlling the flight accurately over a distance of a quarter-million miles. The hazards to man in space—weightlessness and radiation—must be overcome. Equipment must be designed to operate in a "hard" vacuum—much more rarefied than any vacuum that can be created on earth. The hostile environment of the moon must be conquered. Ways must be found for three men, inside the spacecraft, to conduct a countdown that occupies upwards of a hundred workers on earth and launch their return rocket from the barren surface of the moon. Finally, insulating materials must be developed to protect the craft from the searing heat of entry into the earth's atmosphere at a speed of 25,000 miles an hour.

As its command center for technical work on the spacecraft and training of the astronauts, the National Aeronautics and Space Administration is building a manned space flight laboratory near Houston, Texas, on 1000 acres of land obtained from Rice University. As facilities become ready, personnel and func-

tions are moving to Houston from the Space Task Group at
Langley Field, Virginia, headquarters of Project Mercury. The
site borders on a salt-water canal to the Gulf of Mexico.

The giant rockets will be constructed at the Michoud Ordnance Plant near New Orleans, Louisiana, to be operated by
an industrial contractor under the technical direction of the
NASA Marshall Space Flight Center at Huntsville, Alabama.
The New Orleans plant, on 846 acres of land, is adjacent to
the Michoud Canal, which is large enough for ocean-going
barges. The canal connects with the Gulf Intracoastal Waterway
and to a new waterway under construction, the Mississippi River
Gulf Outlet Canal. Built in World War II for the construction
of ocean-going ships, the plant was actually used for plywood
airplanes. The rockets will be ground-tested at a site across the
river in southern Mississippi.

The rockets will be launched from the Air Force Missile
Test Center at Cape Canaveral, Florida. To make room for the
rockets, NASA purchased an additional 80,000 acres north and
west of the reservation as it existed up to 1961. The Air Force
administers the reservation as the national manager of the Atlantic Missile Range, used by all three military services as well
as the civilian space administration. The expansion permits the
construction of at least six new launching complexes if necessary. Circles of up to ten miles in radius must be cleared of
private activity around the launch complexes.

Thus the United States has a complex of centers in warm
climate and connected by waterways for the lunar landing assignment. The warm climate will make it possible to do a maximum of work outdoors the year around. Water transportation
is essential because the rocket stages will be too big for movement any other way. The lunar landing spacecraft, which is
not quite so large, could be transported by land or air. But
Space Administrator Webb chose the location of the manned
space flight center near Houston so that much larger spacecraft
can be developed there if the nation wants them. He believes
the time may be ripe by 1965 to begin work on a ten- or twelve-
man orbiting space station. The availability of year-round water
transportation between centers gives the United States a major
advantage in the race for the moon with the Soviet Union.

Three major categories of technical problems—propulsion,
guidance and environment—must be solved to land men on the

moon. But the greatest problem of all will not be technical. It will be to maintain a high level of support over a period of many years, in good years and bad. Rocket and space development projects cannot be turned on and off like water from a spigot. Teams of scientists and engineers require many months and sometimes years to assemble. Nothing is more wasteful than repeated starts and stops such as took place in the American missile programs of the 1950s.

"Let it be clear that I am asking the Congress and the country to accept a firm commitment to a new course of action—a course which will last for many years and carry very heavy costs," President Kennedy said in proposing the lunar expedition. "If we were to go only halfway, or reduce our sights in the face of difficulty, it would be better not to go at all."

II THE EARLY SPACE YEARS

3. THE BEGINNINGS

THE INVENTOR OF THE ROCKET, a Chinese whose name is lost to history, may have lived before the beginning of the Christian era. However, the earliest recorded use seems to have been in 1232 A.D. by the defenders of the city of Kaifung-fu, to propel flaming arrows against Mongol besiegers. Apparently, Oriental armies had begun using rockets for signal purposes some time earlier. The art spread to Europe by way of Byzantium, and a war rocket was used as early as 1258 at Cologne, Germany.

The earliest rockets were remarkably similar to the skyrockets still fired in the United States in celebration of the Fourth of July—although the brilliant display at the highest point of flight is a more modern invention. They were rolled paper tubes, filled with gunpowder. Rapid flow of hot gas out the rear opening, as a result of the burning of the gunpowder, generated force that propelled the rocket.

One of the oldest misconceptions about rocket propulsion is that it operates by pushing the hot gas against the air outside. This is not true. As a matter of fact, a rocket reaches its highest efficiency in a vacuum, in which there is no air to push against. Sir Isaac Newton explained the principle involved in the third of his famous three laws of motion, declaring that for every action force, there exists a reaction force, equal to the action and pointed in the opposite direction. The most familiar example of action and reaction is the recoil of a gun. As the bullet is propelled forward, the gun is propelled backward with equal force. (But the force gives less acceleration to the gun, since it is heavier than the bullet.) A rocket shoots gas out the rear nozzle and is propelled forward with equal and opposite force.

The first rockets spewed fire in all directions and it is easy to imagine they were fearsome weapons. But medieval weaponeers soon discovered that the psychological advantages were greater than the real ones. For there was no assurance that the rocket would fly in the direction it was pointed. The guided missile was still centuries ahead of them. The slightest deviation of the gas flow from a line directed straight backwards caused the rocket to curve in flight and miss the target by a wide margin. The gun, on the other hand, had a barrel that enabled it to be aimed quite accurately. Thus, the development of weapons for several centuries revolved largely around the improvement of guns.

The first successful use of rockets in war apparently was by troops of the Indian state of Mysore against British colonial troops in the 1780s and 90s. The Indians built rockets weighing 6 to 12 pounds by substituting an iron pipe for the pasteboard tube formerly used to contain the powder. A range of up to a mile or more was reported. A long stick helped to stabilize the rocket in flight.

When news of the Indian rockets spread to Europe, it revived military interest there. Shortly after the turn of the century, a British colonel, William Congreve, began serious work with metal-chambered rockets that led to the development of weapons used widely in the Napoleonic wars. Congreve rockets weighing up to 42 pounds, carrying metal balls as heavy as 18 pounds or bombs weighing as much as 12 pounds, helped the British capture the cities of Boulogne, Copenhagen, Danzig and Leipzig.

But probably the most decisive use of rocket power in that period was in the 1814 battle of Bladensburg, Maryland, in which two American regiments were routed by rocket fire, leaving Washington unprotected. As a result, the capital was captured and burned by the British forces. A short time later, British land and sea forces attempted unsuccessfully to capture Fort McHenry in Baltimore harbor. Their weaponry is recorded in the words of "The Star Spangled Banner."

Congreve's rockets, with a range up to 3000 yards, were just about as effective as the cannons of their time, and the costs were comparable. But he had carried the rocket based on the old black powder almost to its ultimate. An American, William Hale, made one further improvement in the nineteenth century. Instead of using a stick for guidance, Hale put inclined metal vanes in the exhaust nozzle, which caused the rocket to spin rapidly and gain gyroscopic stability. Hale rockets were used by American troops in the Mexican War. However, they never were very reliable.

Meanwhile, rapid advances were made in artillery. Within a short time after Congreve's death in 1826, artillery developed far greater range and far greater accuracy than the biggest rockets. In addition, artillery became much more reliable. The overwhelming superiority that artillery held in the nineteenth century is best symbolized by the fact that in Jules Verne's novel, *From the Earth to the Moon*, the space ship is propelled by firing it from a gigantic gun.

Others, however, took up the idea of using rockets to travel beyond the atmosphere. Hermann Ganswindt, an early German aviation prophet, proposed in the early 1890s that the reaction principle might be used in space. At about the same time in Russia, Konstantin Tsiolkovski began writing on the subject and proposed the use of kerosene as a liquid rocket fuel.

A boy in Worcester, Massachusetts, had similar ideas. In 1898, at the age of sixteen, Robert H. Goddard began keeping notes of his ideas on rockets and, three years later, wrote an article on space navigation that was rejected by a popular magazine on science. Later, as a member of the physics faculty of Clark University, Goddard proved mathematically and by experiment that a rocket will function in vacuum. During the same period, he obtained two patents on rocket propulsion—the first of many.

Goddard obtained $5000 from the Smithsonian Institution to support his research in 1917 and, with a war on, the U.S. Signal Corps granted aid in the following year. A new and more efficient explosive powder, based on nitroglycerin and nitrocellulose, had been developed. Goddard and an Army officer, Charles N. Hickman, demonstrated rockets burning the new powder in November, 1918, at Aberdeen Proving Ground, Maryland, but the work was dropped after the armistice.

After the war, Goddard concentrated on liquid propellants, with which there was the possibility of controlling the rate of flow and thus the rate of burning. He may have been influenced by the writings of the Russian, Tsiolkovski. Gasoline was the natural choice for fuel, because of its low price and the fact that a great deal was known about its properties from using it in automobile motors. But a rocket must carry its own air to support combustion. Goddard proposed the use of oxygen in liquid form—which must be kept at a temperature of 228° below zero Fahrenheit.

He outlined the plan in a report for the Smithsonian entitled "A Method of Reaching Extreme Altitudes," which the institution published in 1919. Several dozen copies of the report reached Germany. One was read by a young Rumanian living in Germany, named Hermann Oberth. With Smithsonian funds, Goddard tested the idea over the next few years until, on March 16, 1926, he flew the world's first liquid-fueled rocket 184 feet at Auburn, Massachusetts.

Goddard continued his experiments but was constantly running out of money. Besides that, the authorities in the heavily populated Massachusetts area had strong misgivings about the safety of rockets, and he resolved to set up operations in a more isolated area. In 1929, Charles A. Lindbergh, the aviator, heard of Goddard's work, visited him and later persuaded Daniel Guggenheim to make Guggenheim Foundation funds available.* Goddard moved his operations to a lonely tract of land near Roswell, New Mexico. From 1929 to 1941, Goddard received more than $150,000 from the foundation.

During the entire period between the two World Wars, Goddard made frequent proposals that the Army and Navy support his work with the idea of developing large liquid-fueled rockets, but they never took the suggestions seriously. The Goddard-Hickman work with the double-base (nitroglycerin-nitrocellulose) solid propellant rockets lay completely dormant until 1933, when a single Army officer, Captain L. A. Skinner, became interested in the subject and began experiments again at Aberdeen Proving Ground.

In Germany, meanwhile, wide interest had developed in rockets as the result of writings by Hermann Oberth and others.

* One of the plans to be accomplished with Guggenheim Foundation funds was to fire rockets up to altitudes of 50 miles during the Second International Polar Year in 1932-33, carrying instruments designed by the Carnegie Institution of Washington to investigate the ionosphere. However, the worldwide depression made it necessary to cut back on many of the more elaborate Polar Year plans.

By 1929, a motion picture, *Frau in Mond (The Girl in the Moon)*, on space travel was successfully produced. Oberth and his friends formed the German Rocket Society (Verein fuer Raumschiffahrt—abbreviated VfR) in 1927 and opened an experimental launching station near Berlin in 1930. Liquid-fueled rockets, based on the Goddard principles, were launched at two sites in Germany the following year.

During this period, rockets came to the attention of the German Army general staff. The idea of developing rocket weapons had a decisive argument in its favor: Although almost every form of weapon development was prohibited by the Treaty of Versailles, rockets were not mentioned. On December 13, 1930, the high command put Captain Doctor Walter Dornberger in charge of rocket studies, which led to the establishment of an army ordnance development program in 1932. Wernher von Braun—one of the VfR group—was hired as the first employee.

Rocket groups were formed in the Soviet Union, France and the United States during these years too. Tsiolkovski and friends formed the Soviet group, the Society for Studying Interplanetary Communications, in 1924. The French group, a committee of the French Astronomy Society, first met in 1927. Goddard did not take part in the American Society, which was organized by G. Edward Pendray and David Lasser in 1930 as the American Interplanetary Society. The name was changed in 1934 to the American Rocket Society.

Both the Soviet and American groups fired their first rockets in 1933, the year of the formation of the British Interplanetary Society. But these were amateurs—enthusiasts working in their spare time. Progress did not take place very fast. Some time in the 1930s, the Soviet government began to give greater support to rocket work, however. A glider, propelled by a rocket burning nitric acid and kerosene, is reported to have been flown by Soviet scientists in 1939.

The German work moved ahead at a much faster pace. At the Berlin suburb of Kuemmersdorf in 1934, the Army group fired a rocket designated as A-2 a distance of two miles.

Two years later, design work was completed on the A-3, an assembly 21 feet tall and weighing 1650 pounds when fully loaded with liquid oxygen and alcohol fuel. Since the A-3 had an expected range up to 10 or 15 miles, a launching site away from populated areas was needed. Von Braun, a native of East

Prussia, suggested the island of Usedom, which separates the Bay of Stettin from the Baltic Sea near the village of Peenemuende. The Army and Air Force jointly funded purchase of the island in 1937.

Three A-3 rockets were fired from Peenemuende in the fall of 1937. The rocket engines themselves operated well, but once again, as so often in the history of rocketry, the guidance and control system was inadequate. To control flight direction, the A-3 had movable vanes inside the combustion chamber. Investigation showed later that the method did not provide enough adjustment and the reactions were too slow. The next year, a new rocket, the A-5, with the same powerplant but a new control system, was tested successfully. The new control system added external fins, which corrected the flight path by reaction against the air stream, just as the rudder and ailerons control the flight of an airplane.

Altogether, Von Braun's group flew 25 of the A-5 rockets over the Baltic to test the concept of a much bigger rocket, the A-4, which was designed to carry a warhead of 2200 pounds (a metric ton) to a distance of 160 miles—twice the range of the "Big Bertha" Paris gun, the longest-range weapon of World War I. The A-4 stood 47 feet tall, atop a 5-foot firing table, for a total height of 52 feet. Loaded with something over 19,000 pounds of liquid oxygen and alcohol, it weighed more than 28,000 pounds.

Actual work on the A-4 began in early 1940. A brief slowdown occurred that summer, when Adolf Hitler took it off the priority list, but the German general staff quietly kept the operation at Peenemuende going. Flight tests began June 13, 1942. The missile was ready for action by September, 1944, a few months after the Luftwaffe's Fi-103, a pilotless aircraft that came to be known in London as the "buzz-bomb." Hitler's propaganda ministry called the two the Vergeltung (vengeance) weapons. The buzz-bomb was named Vengeance 1, or V-1; the A-4 rocket became V-2. Altogether, 1027 V-2s were launched, most of them against London, with a failure rate of only 7.7 per cent.

In America and Britain, meanwhile, the military services concentrated on solid-propellant rockets. The British War Office held a meeting to review the subject in 1934. In 1936, the royal arsenal was directed to begin rocket research. By the time World War II had begun, the British program had assumed sufficient importance that Prime Minister Winston Churchill attended several tests at the Aberporth rocket establishment. Churchill demanded a personal weekly report on progress for more than a year afterward.

As war preparation began in the United States, the military services resumed rocket work in July, 1940, with the establishment of a laboratory at Indian Head, Maryland, about 20 miles southeast of Washington. The National Defense Research Committee put Charles N. Hickman, who had worked with Goddard in World War I, in charge. Captain Skinner, the Army Ordnance officer who had been working with rockets at Aberdeen, was assigned as a liaison officer at Indian Head. Under Hickman and Skinner, Captain E. G. Uhl developed the Bazooka rocket, which used a double-base solid propellant like that produced in the World War I experiments. The Bazooka, weighing 3.4 pounds and fired from a launcher weighing 13.3 pounds, was capable of penetrating 3 to 5 inches of steel and was extremely effective against tanks. The lack of recoil made it possible for a single infantryman to launch a Bazooka from his shoulder.

The defense research committee expanded U.S. rocket work in 1941 by contracts with the California Institute of Technology, George Washington University, the Budd Wheel Company and Bell Telephone Laboratories. The following year, the Army established a rocket laboratory at Aberdeen. As its work grew, the Indian Head group was moved to Cumberland, Maryland, where it was established as the Allegany Ballistic Laboratory under a Navy contract with George Washington University. After the war, Hercules Powder Company took over the operation.

The Guggenheim Aeronautical Laboratory of the California Institute of Technology (GALCIT) had been working since 1939 on a related problem—the use of jet or rocket propulsion to help airplanes take off in a shorter time and less runway length than with just the regular engines. The group, under the direction of Doctor Theodore von Kármán, became better known under its Cal Tech title, the Jet Propulsion Laboratory (JPL). A number of new solid-propellant formulations, slower burning and more stable than the older double-base variety, were developed by JPL. The burning rate had to be slowed to less than that of existing double-base powder to give enough force to aid the take-off without ripping the rocket from the body of the plane. Some liquid rockets were developed for the same purpose.

The Army Air Corps asked von Kármán to set up mass-production facilities for the JATO (jet assisted takeoff) rockets. The result was the formation of Aerojet Engineering Company. The Navy, because of its special need for extra power in taking planes off from carriers, soon became the largest customer.

British and American groups worked together during World War II on small airborne rockets and both countries developed rocket weapons for use on naval vessels. The only work on liquid-propelled rockets outside JPL was at Reaction Motors Incorporated, a firm formed just after the beginning of the war by a group of American Rocket Society engineers in Pompton Lakes, New Jersey, and at a Navy research center at Annapolis.

The Russians and Japanese both used solid-propellant rockets in World War II. The Russians are reported to have used small rockets extensively in the defense of Stalingrad. The most notable Japanese application was a fairly large rocket that gave a Kamikaze suicide plane a final burst of speed as it plunged toward its target.

When Red Army forces approached Peenemuende in the spring of 1945, von Braun and around one hundred members of the planning staff—including almost all the founders of the VfR—fled to the west and surrendered to American forces in Bavaria. American forces also captured an underground V-2 production factory near Niedersachswerfen. By agreement, this area was to be under Russian occupation. But before it was turned over, the U.S. Army had shipped 300 carloads of V-2 components and equipment to the United States. The von Braun group and some other specialists were also brought to America under an operation called "Paperclip."

Russia captured most of the production engineers at Peenemuende—a far more numerous group than the planning staff—and thus had equal access to German ballistic missile technology. The Germans were held for as long as ten years after the end of the war. But they were not actually put to work on missile development projects. They were kept available for consultation about how they had solved individual problems at Peenemuende. Then, when the Soviets were convinced they had milked the Germans dry, they were sent home. Some of the Germans were quite surprised to learn afterward that Russia had extensive ballistic missile programs.

The United States shipped its 300 carloads of V-2 parts to a rocket testing station established by the Army Ordnance Corps a

year previously in the New Mexico desert southwest of Alamo-
gordo near the White Sands National Monument—and not far
from the site where the first atomic bomb was tested in that same
summer of 1945. For the first years after the war, the Army, in a
project called Hermes, concentrated on learning all about the
V-2. However, the American who could have helped the most,
Robert H. Goddard, died that summer. He had spent the war at
the Navy's Annapolis rocket station.

While the Army experimented with the V-2, the Navy put its
research laboratory and the Martin Company to work developing the Viking, a rocket like the V-2 but about half its size,
which was to be launched from ship as well as shore installations. The Viking and a yet smaller liquid rocket, the Aerobee,
became standard vehicles for research into the upper atmosphere. The Viking reached altitudes of about 150 miles, while
the Aerobee reached about 100 miles.

One of the important milestones in the history of rocketry
took place at White Sands May 13, 1948, when Army Ordnance
launched the first two-stage rocket. Staging rockets was a tremendous step forward because a comparatively small second stage
might add a huge increase in rocket speed. The first two-stage
rockets were not particularly successful. But the fifth shot, on
February 24, 1949, proved that the two-stage principle could
accomplish what its supporters claimed.

The V-2 first stage, which weighed 28,000 pounds gross, generated 57,000 pounds thrust until its 19,000 pounds of fuel and
oxygen were expended 40 seconds later. After separation the
empty V-2 rose to a height of 63 miles. Then the little second-
stage Wac Corporal—gross weight 665 pounds—took over. Its
engine generated 1500 pounds thrust for another 45 seconds. As
a result, the payload attained a speed of 5150 miles per hour and
climbed to an altitude of 250 miles. The speed attained was
about 30 per cent of that necessary for a satellite to go into orbit
around the earth. It was more than a third of that required for
an ocean-spanning missile.

Three years previously, the Air Force had contracted with
Consolidated Vultee Aircraft Company (Convair) to study rocket
capabilities with the idea of developing an intercontinental missile. However, the contract was dropped during an economy
wave in 1947; Convair continued some parts of the work with
its own funds. The Air Force did not revive the project until

1951; even then, the project—called Atlas—proceeded with limited funds for three more years.

Russia, however, did not delay. The first Soviet nuclear bomb was exploded in the late summer of 1949. A short time thereafter, Josef Stalin ordered full-scale development of a rocket large enough to launch the bomb against the United States.

It is always a temptation, when recording a lengthy history of related events, to pick one out and say "there was a turning-point." There were many turning-points in the history of rockets and space exploration: Goddard's change from solid to liquid fuels after World War I; the German Army decision to support rocket work; the first two-stage rockets at White Sands; Stalin's authorization of an ICBM.

But perhaps an even more significant turning-point took place April 5, 1950, at a small dinner party in a suburban home near Washington, at which rockets may not have been mentioned more than in passing. The party was at the home of James A. Van Allen, a thirty-five-year-old professor at the Applied Physics Laboratory of Johns Hopkins University near his home in Silver Spring, Maryland. Van Allen, a specialist in upper-air research, had invited a group of colleagues for an evening of talk with Sydney Chapman, a distinguished visiting geophysicist from Oxford.

The guests included geophysicists Lloyd V. Berkner, J. Wallace Joyce, S. Fred Singer and Ernest H. Vestine. A major topic of discussion during the evening was what all the scientists agreed was a need of numerous simultaneous observations at many points around the earth, so that conclusions might be drawn about the earth as a whole and the over-all effect of the sun and the other outside influences.

"I proposed that perhaps the only solution was to organize a third international polar year," Berkner recalled nine years later. The polar years, in 1882 and 1932, were combined endeavors by the world of science to make observations in the inaccessible polar regions, by sending expeditions to many places simultaneously.

The suggestion, which Berkner made on the spur of the moment, was taken up enthusiastically. He and Chapman agreed to present it at a meeting that summer of an international scientific body, the Mixed Commission on the Ionosphere.

The result of the Van Allen dinner party was that wheels were set in motion for the organization of a great international scientific endeavor, later designated the International Geophysical Year. A major goal was the observation and analysis of relationships between the earth and activity of the sun. And so the time chosen was the eighteen-month period from July, 1957, to December, 1958, which scientists knew would be a time of maximum solar activity.

The proposal passed through a half-dozen international scientific gatherings in the next few years, winning almost unanimous support everywhere. The early stages of preparation involved very little expense, beyond the travel costs of the delegates involved and the normal expenses of the scientific societies. Later, governments were to be asked to spend larger sums.

How is all this related to space exploration? The International Geophysical Year provided the framework and justification for extensive government support of rocket launching and development, primarily for the purpose of space exploration. Ever since the end of World War II, rocket enthusiasts had been agitating for satellite launchings. The U.S. Air Force in 1946 began satellite studies which Secretary of Defense James V. Forrestal disclosed in December, 1948. But all such projects were confined to paper until the IGY became a reality.

Fred Singer, a young geophysicist who was among those present at the Van Allen dinner, was the first American scientist to propose that a satellite be launched during the IGY. At the Fourth International Congress on Astronautics at Zurich, Switzerland, in August, 1953, Singer outlined a project he called MOUSE (Minimum Orbital Unmanned Satellite Experiment), an instrument package weighing 100 pounds. Singer pressed his idea with leading U.S. scientists during the next year.

Meanwhile, the von Braun German group moved to Redstone Arsenal, Alabama, from Fort Bliss, Texas, in 1950. The next year, the Germans began working on the development of the Redstone missile, an improved, longer range version of the V-2. When talk about launching satellites started they began to lay plans to use their new rocket. On June 25, 1954, von Braun met with several government officials and scientists to formalize a plan, which they called Project Orbiter. They agreed that a two-stage rocket composed of the Redstone and a small Navy rocket, the Loki, could launch a 5-pound satellite without major development, on relatively short notice. If an official project were established to develop a larger second stage, they reported, a heavier satellite with more instruments might be launched. Army and Navy representatives approved the project August 3 and authorized letting contracts for procurement of components.

During the same period, a series of statements emanating from the Soviet Union indicated that the idea of space exploration was under consideration there too. On November 27, 1953, A. N. Nesmeyanov of the USSR Academy of Sciences said science had reached the stage that artificial satellites and launchings to the moon were possible. In March, 1954, Moscow Radio urged Soviet youth to be the first to reach the moon. The Moscow Air Club formed a section in April to study interplanetary flight.

In September, 1954, at the urging of Berkner and Singer, the International Union of Radio Societies (URSI) passed a resolution urging governments to launch satellites during the IGY. Later that month, they went to Rome for a meeting of the Special Committee of the IGY. During that meeting, Berkner invited a group of influential U.S. scientists to an apartment he had rented at the Hotel Majestic—so as to hear Singer's proposal.

Those present included Joseph Kaplan, Athelstan Spilhaus, Harry Wexler, John Adkins, Allen Shapley, Hugh Odishaw, N. C. Gerson, J. Wallace Joyce and Homer E. Newell. Some had serious doubts whether the project was practical. Newell suggested that the batteries supplying power might bubble in the vacuum of space.

"Damn it!" shouted Spilhaus, banging his fist upon a table, "we'll get batteries that don't bubble!"

The meeting continued far into the night as Singer discussed in detail the questions of orbits, the effect of launching errors, lifetimes, telemetering and satellite orientation, problems of receiving stations and geophysical and astrophysical applications, as well as power supplies.

"I must say that after the long technical analysis," Berkner remarked, "I believe there was a unanimous agreement on the part of all those present that it was a feasible project." The discussion then turned to the political aspects. Berkner and Spilhaus soon convinced most of the others that launching a satellite would have tremendous implications for a nation's prestige in the world and that the United States could not afford to be left behind. The only doubts expressed were that a program to launch a satellite might endanger the program of launching many scientific rockets for high-altitude research during the eighteen-month IGY period.

As a result, the American delegation introduced, and the special committee adopted a resolution that read as follows:

"In view of the great importance of observations during extended periods of time of terrestrial radiations and geophysical phenomena in the upper atmosphere, and in view of the advanced state of present rocket techniques, CSAGI (the special committee) recommends that thought be given to the launching of small satellite vehicles, to their scientific instrumentation, and to the new problems associated with satellite experiments, such as power supply, telemetering and orientation of the vehicle."

The Soviet delegates to the meeting took no part in the discussion. "They didn't object," Berkner recalled. "They didn't say anything."

It was the action of the IGY committee that tipped the balance in favor of an American program aimed at exploring space. The only extensive rocket work in the United States was conducted by the military services. But Secretary of Defense Charles E. Wilson, the highest military authority, was firmly opposed to space exploration, and felt a satellite launching to be a useless stunt. On November 17, 1954, he told a press conference he had no knowledge of U.S. scientists working on satellites and said he would not be alarmed if the USSR built one first.

However, the American public responded favorably to the idea—partly because of numerous books, magazine articles and films that had been produced on the subject since the war's end. In the months after the Rome meeting, public discussion increased and, in December, Walt Disney produced a film, *Man in Space*. In March, the U.S. National Committee for the IGY reported after study that earth satellites were feasible and urged approval of the idea by the National Academy of Sciences and the National Science Foundation. Alan T. Waterman, president of the academy, took the proposal to the White House later that month. Thus, presented with the support of science and the opposition of the military, President Eisenhower approved the project as a purely scientific endeavor.

In the Soviet Union, no such objections existed. The work on developing large rockets had gone far since its beginning four or five years previously. On April 15, 1955, a Soviet newspaper disclosed the formation of a permanent commission within the

USSR Academy of Sciences for "coordinating work on the solution of the problems of mastering cosmic space," including plans for developing an earth satellite. Something over three months later, Eisenhower finally approved the U.S. plan, patterned after Singer's MOUSE project. The National Academy of Sciences and the National Science Foundation made the announcement at the White House July 29, 1955. The Soviet Union announced the following day that it also planned a satellite—and had been working on the problem for some time. Nikita Khrushchev, then one of a duumvirate ruling the USSR—the other member was Bulganin—offered on August 2 to cooperate with the United States if the project were in the interest of mankind. There is no record of any U.S. response.

President Eisenhower directed the Department of Defense to conduct the satellite development program, in cooperation with the academy and the foundation. The first decision to be made was what kind of rocket was to be used. The Army-Navy Project Orbiter was not the only candidate. Earlier in 1955, when Orbiter first came to his attention, Secretary Wilson had discovered that there were two other satellite projects in the planning stage: an Air Force proposal to use the still undeveloped Atlas ICBM and a Naval Research Laboratory plan to use a rocket based on the Viking. Wilson told Donald A. Quarles, his assistant secretary for research and development, to coordinate the plans; the services were forbidden to commit any money for such projects without Quarles's approval. The assistant secretary turned the problem over to a scientific committee headed by Homer J. Stewart of the Jet Propulsion Laboratory.

Before the President approved the plan for launching a satellite the question was considered by the National Security Council, the nation's highest policy-making body. The council approved the plan only with the proviso that the project should not interfere with the nation's missile program. For by that time, intelligence reports had indicated that the USSR was well ahead of the United States in its work on intercontinental missiles.

The Stewart committee soon eliminated the Atlas from its consideration, because the Air Force could make no promise that an Atlas would be available during the eighteen-month period of the IGY. The selection between Orbiter and the Viking plan, however, was more difficult. The Orbiter plan, based on the Redstone, seemed to have more weight-carrying capacity. But the Naval Research Laboratory had a long and outstanding history of developing scientific instruments. NRL scientists had conducted very successful upper-air research with its Viking and Aerobee rockets since the end of World War II.

At one point of the deliberations, the committee considered assigning the rocket to the Army and the instruments to the Navy. But as C. C. Furnas, one member, recalled later: "We knew of the unwillingness of one branch of the service to contribute personnel, money—or even information at times—to a project for which some other branch would get most of the credit. . . . If the job was to be done in a hurry, it had to go to a single branch of service."

On September 9, 1955, the committee decided, by a vote of seven to two, to support the Naval Research Laboratory plan, based on the Viking. The Department of Defense approved the recommendation. A month later, the Martin Company, which had developed the Viking rocket, was given a prime contract to modify it.

As a result of the Stewart committee recommendation (Stewart, himself, was one of the two in the minority; Furnas was the other), the Army was directed to stop work on its satellite launcher. However, von Braun found a pretext on which work might be continued. The Army agency was just then beginning research on the Jupiter intermediate-range ballistic missile (IRBM), which had an intended range of 1500 miles. One of the problems to be solved for a missile of such long range was that of re-entry—that is, designing the warhead so that it would not burn up like a meteor upon returning to the atmosphere from space. Such a problem hardly existed for the Redstone, which, by itself, had a range of only 200 miles.

Von Braun's engineers conceived the notion of using the Redstone with upper stages to simulate the re-entry conditions that would be encountered by the one-stage Jupiter. Since it was one of a series of projects in support of the Jupiter program, they called it Jupiter-C. However, the Jupiter-C was much more powerful than required. On its first flight, a year later, it carried a test nose cone more than twice the 1500 miles required.

The Navy project was given the name of Vanguard and modest funds. John P. Hagen, director of the Naval Research Laboratory, was given charge. A few months after work began, he requested a top priority, so that he would have first call on materials and services. On April 2, 1956, the Navy asked the Department of Defense to assign the then highest "S" priority to Vanguard. On May 29, the department approved a listing of Vanguard as item No. 1, category 1. Thus it was outranked by category S Programs, such as ICBM and IRBM, but it ranked higher than other military procurement. Jupiter-C, as a part of the Jupiter IRBM program, enjoyed the highest priority.

Developing the three-stage Vanguard rocket took longer than expected. The first stage, an enlarged version of the Viking, was not flown until October 23, 1957. The second, a modification of the Aerobee, was not ready to fly until December, 1957. The third stage, using solid propellant, was ready a little sooner. It passed muster on flight atop a Viking on May 1, 1957.

But there is much more to a satellite program than building the rockets. The satellite itself, with its scientific instruments, power supplies and radio transmitter, must be tested. Launching facilities must be built. Specially designed radar must be installed at the launching station and at several stations on its initial track. Receiving stations must be set up to track the satellite and collect its scientific information. The Vanguard project accomplished all of these tasks within the time assigned. Cape Canaveral, until then restricted to ballistic missile work, was converted to space.

While the Vanguard work dragged on, the Army asked again and again for permission to launch a satellite with the Jupiter-C. Just as regularly, permission was refused. In May, 1957, Andrew Stone of the motion-picture firm Metro-Goldwyn-Mayer appeared at the Pentagon and offered to pay the cost of launching a satellite with a Jupiter-C. The proposal was, of course, rejected.

On June 2, an article in *Pravda* quoted Professor Nesmeyanov as saying that the rockets and instruments for the Soviet satellite were complete and that it would be used for ionospheric studies. On June 9, the USSR *Literary Gazette* said dogs would take part in the Soviet space program. In the June issue of *Radio,* a Soviet magazine intended for amateur radio operators, an article announced that the satellite would transmit at frequencies of 20 and 40 megacycles.

Fifty-six days after the beginning of the IGY, on August 26,

1957, the Soviet Union announced it had successfully flown an intercontinental ballistic missile, which it said could be directed to any part of the world. In the same announcement, the Soviets reported they had conducted a series of nuclear and thermonuclear explosions at very high altitude. Three days later, the U.S. Department of Defense said in Washington that from four to six Soviet ICBM tests had taken place the previous spring. At this time, only one attempt had been made to launch the U.S. Atlas ICBM, on June 11, and it exploded a few moments after takeoff. It was not until December, 1957, that the Atlas had a successful flight—of only 600 miles. The first successful Atlas flight with all engines in operation was a year later, on August 2, 1958. This flight traveled 2500 miles. Fifteen months after the Soviet announcement, on November 28, 1958, an Atlas missile finally traveled full range and landed in the South Atlantic 6325 miles from Cape Canaveral.

Having completed development of its ICBM, Russia then adapted it for satellite launchings. On October 4, from an undisclosed point,* Soviet scientists launched the earth's first artificial satellite, a polished aluminum sphere weighing 184 pounds, with a diameter of 22.8 inches. It had four antennas. It traveled around the earth in 96.2 minutes on an orbit with apogee of 558 miles and perigee of 142 miles. The plane of the orbit was inclined 65° to the equator. The Russians affectionately called it a "devoted companion" in space. The word in Russian was "sputnik."

Thirty days later, Russia launched a much larger satellite, which contained a pressurized cabin carrying a female dog named Laika and instruments to record her reactions. Sputnik II, a payload of 1120 pounds attached to a rocket body weighing four tons, traveled in an orbit with perigee of 140 miles and apogee of 1038 miles. The inclination again was 65°.

Sputnik I, whose radio operated twenty-three days, provided information on the density and temperature of the upper atmosphere. It circled the earth for about ninety-five days. The radios of Sputnik II operated for seven days, sending back information that led to the discovery that the sun affects the density of the upper atmosphere. It also measured concentrations of electrons in the outer ionosphere, measured cosmic rays and provided

* Probably Kara-Kul-Bulak in the Kazakh S.S.R. See Chapter Seven.

"bio-medical" information on the reaction of the dog to the weightless condition that exists while a satellite is in the free fall of orbital flight. Sputnik II came down after more than five months in orbit, on April 14, 1958.

4. THE FIRST SATELLITES

The LAUNCHING OF SPUTNIK, the first object hurled by man into outer space, marked the beginning of a new period of human history, leading inevitably to manned flight beyond the earth's atmosphere. It also marked the beginning of a new phase of relationships between nations on earth. Before October 4, 1957, the Soviet Union appeared to friends, neutrals and foes as vigorous but technologically a backward country. The United States, whatever her faults, seemed to be the world leader in science and technology.

If America had launched the first satellite, the world would still have been electrified. But the event would not have caused shocked surprise. America's Vanguard program was the subject of extensive publicity. Several books and hundreds of newspaper and magazine articles had appeared before the three-stage rocket was little more than an idea on paper. Russia had also announced satellite plans, but it had hardly occurred to anyone that she would succeed first.

If the Soviets could launch a satellite ahead of America, people around the world wondered, were they not also ahead of America in developing long-range missiles? This inevitably led to questions whether the balance of world power had undergone a fundamental change. Before Sputnik, there was no serious doubt in the world's capitals that the Western Alliance held the military upper hand through technological superiority. Everyone believed that the combination of U.S. and British planes carrying nuclear bombs, and bases ringing the Soviet

[55

Union, more than made up for the excess of military manpower available to the Communist side.

But if, with the advent of the long-range missile, Russia could wipe out the Western technological advantage, the greater manpower of the Communist bloc suddenly assumed new importance. And if Russia pulled ahead of the United States in technology, the way seemed clear for the Soviet Union to dominate the world. Of course, Russia did not pull ahead of the United States technologically on October 4, 1957. America still had much more of steel capacity, food production, chemical industry and almost all the other factors that make for a strong industrial economy. In direct military strength, the United States still had more and better aircraft—and air power would remain the most important strategic factor for several years to come.

In peacetime world politics, however, the actual military strength of a nation is often not as important as what it appears to be. Sputnik made the Soviet Union *appear* to be strong and growing stronger. The Russian custom of secrecy reinforced the impression. Russia announced only her missile and satellite successes—never the failures. In America, both successes and failures were reported—for a long time, mostly failures.

Furthermore, Russian propaganda made the most of the scientific, peaceful aspects of space exploration. Soviet publicity sought to create the image of a young, vigorous nation attempting challenging tasks. It sought to leave an impression of Russia as a "comer" in technology, in comparison with a lazy, tired United States that no longer cared enough to explore the unknown.

Within the United States, the reaction was shock and outraged pride. Editors, congressmen and other opinion leaders demanded to know why. The educational system came under question. Scientists renewed their demands for more support of basic research. Military missile and space programs were assured of a virtual blank check.

Recognizing that the country had suffered a propaganda reverse, President Eisenhower's administration reacted with two steps. First, the Navy's Vanguard program was given high priority with the aim of launching a satellite as soon as possible. Several weeks later, the Army and Air Force were authorized to proceed with their satellite-launching plans.

John P. Hagen, chief of Vanguard, told his superiors the pro-

gram had reached a phase at which, if progress continued, a
test satellite might be launched within three months. The prediction was certainly optimistic. Neither the first nor the second
stage of the three-stage Vanguard rocket had yet been flown.
The third stage had flown only once, as a second stage atop another rocket. Nevertheless, the launching facilities had been installed at Cape Canaveral, Florida, a worldwide network of
radio tracking stations had been constructed and all of the three
stages had been successfully tested on the ground.

Hagen insists that he made quite clear to his superiors the
conditional nature of his prediction, and that he explained at
length that dates are impossible to set firmly in a research and
development program. Nevertheless, President Eisenhower told
a press conference on October 9, without qualification, that a
Vanguard test vehicle would be launched before the end of the
year.

On October 23, Hagen's group launched the Vanguard first
stage, with dummy upper stages. General Electric Company,
which developed the rocket engine under subcontract to the
Martin Company, says that flight marked the first time that a
large liquid-propelled rocket was flown successfully in the United
States on the first attempt.

The first- and third-stage engines having been tested, the next
step was a test of the second stage, newly developed for Vanguard by the Aerojet-General Corporation. The program for the
test called for launching a $3\frac{1}{4}$-pound aluminum sphere into
orbit. If the launching were successful, the sphere would test
components that would be carried later on full-sized Vanguard
satellites.

The public furor in the United States, and the blow to the
nation's prestige abroad, made up a situation that the Eisenhower administration clearly wanted to counteract as soon as
possible. One obvious course of action would be to invite the
press to view the forthcoming Vanguard launching. Hagen advised against it, pointing out that there was no assurance the
launch would succeed.

Nevertheless, even as a risk, there was something to recommend such a step. The psychological damage had already been
done by Russia's success in launching the two Sputniks, and
President Eisenhower had predicted an American satellite would
be launched shortly. If the satellite were not launched in the

time promised, the nation's prestige would suffer anyway. Why not, the argument ran, gamble on scoring a triumph before the biggest possible audience?

The proposal for a gamble won out and Murray Snyder, Defense Department press chief, ordered the Air Force to provide transportation to Cape Canaveral for newsmen desiring to report the launch. As a result, hundreds of reporters were watching on December 6, when the three-stage Vanguard rose to an altitude of 18 inches and fell to pieces when the first stage failed.

The Army, meanwhile, had been developing its own rocket. Although it had no authorization to launch a satellite, the Army Ballistic Missile Agency's team of rocket builders, headed by Wernher von Braun, had nevertheless been developing the rocket assembly they had proposed in 1955, justifying the expense on the ground that the rocket could be used for investigating how missile warhead materials withstand re-entry into the atmosphere from space. As early as September 20, 1956, a three-stage Jupiter-C assembly launched a small payload to an altitude of 680 miles and to a distance of 3300 miles southeastward across the Atlantic Ocean from Cape Canaveral. The Army group used an improved Redstone missile with upper stages that consisted of combinations of a small solid-propellant rocket called "Baby Sergeant," developed by the Jet Propulsion Laboratory at the California Institute of Technology.

For the September, 1956, launching, the Army used a second stage consisting of four Baby Sergeants and the third stage was a single one. It reached a speed of almost 20,000 feet per second —compared with the speed of about 25,000 feet per second required for it to go into orbit. A few more Baby Sergeants obviously would be enough to make that possible. In two subsequent flights, the Jupiter-C development was completed. But the Army had no authorization to launch a satellite.

After Sputnik, with the reversal of the decision, scientific instruments originally intended for Vanguard were installed in a 30.8-pound satellite designed to go aboard the Jupiter-C. One experiment, a set of Geiger counters to measure cosmic rays, was designed by James A. Van Allen of the State University of Iowa. It was the same Van Allen who, seven years previously, had been host to the historic gathering of scientists in Silver Spring, Maryland, at which the first proposal was made for a new special year of coordinated worldwide scientific observations, and which led to the 1957-58 International Geophysical Year.*

On January 31, 1958, eighty-four days after use of the Jupiter-C rocket was authorized, the Army launched Explorer I, America's first and the world's third artificial satellite. It followed an elliptical orbit with apogee of 1594 miles and perigee of 225 miles. The instruments worked perfectly and the radio signals were heard around the world by stations in the Vanguard Minitrack network.

Five days later, the Navy made another attempt to launch a Vanguard satellite. But after 77 seconds of flight, a connection between units of the first-stage control system failed to function and the rocket veered off course, snapped apart and fell. Finally, however, on St. Patrick's Day, another 3¼-pound sphere became the first Vanguard satellite in an orbit with perigee of 406 and apogee of 2463 miles. Because of the height even at perigee, Vanguard I is expected to stay aloft for at least two hundred years. Its radio might stay in operation just as long.

Invidious comparisons were bound to be drawn between the sizes of the Russian and American IGY satellites. Sputnik I weighed 184 pounds. Sputnik II, with its dog passenger, weighed 1120 pounds. Compared with them, Explorer and Vanguard looked pitiful. Strangely enough, the actual scientific results achieved by the American satellites were superior—unless the Russians have made important findings that they choose not to publish. There are some who believe the Russians have done just that—despite the fact that such a practice is self-defeating. For it is only by subjecting important data to experts everywhere that science can arrive at the truth. The interchange of fact and interpretations is a vital part of the process.

The first important discovery of satellite science came when two graduate students of the State University of Iowa were examining tape recordings of the signals transmitted by instruments aboard Explorer I. The Geiger counter appeared to be behaving strangely. Information on cosmic rays, obtained with high-altitude balloons and rocket soundings, indicated that between 30 and 40 cosmic rays would be counted every second in the satellite; thus, the range of the instruments had been set to bracket the 30–40-per-second area.

* And the same Van Allen who had provided experiments for some of the first captured V-2 flights at White Sands in the late 1940s.

But as the satellite climbed from its perigee, the frequency of cosmic-ray counts would rise sharply and then suddenly drop to zero. The students puzzled over this for a while until realization gradually dawned upon them that it actually wasn't falling to zero. Instead, it was saturating the instrument completely so that, for long periods, no cosmic rays were counted.

"Holy cow!" declared Ernest Ray, one of Van Allen's students. "Space is radioactive."

And indeed it is. There are intense zones of radioactivity that begin at altitudes of 500 to 600 miles over the tropics and middle latitudes of the earth. It remained for Van Allen to explain that the zones consist of protons and electrons—charged atomic particles—"trapped" by the earth's magnetic field in huge arc-shaped paths between the poles. The trapping results from the fact that a magnetic field exerts a sideways force, and thus curves the path of any moving thing that has an electric charge. The amount of the sideways force depends, of course, on the strength of the magnetic field.

A charged particle moving in the neighborhood of the earth begins to travel in a spiral path under the influence of the earth's magnetism. But as it heads toward one of the magnetic poles, the field grows steadily more powerful and the spiral becomes tighter as the circular motion grows faster. Finally, at some point near the pole, where the field is strongest, the forward motion is reversed by what physicists call a "magnetic mirror." The particle swings back around the earth in a wide arc and approaches the other pole in the same way. Then the process begins all over again.

It wasn't hard for Van Allen to explain the radiation belts in terms of what scientists already knew of the interaction between charged particles and magnetic fields. But the same interactions would repel any stray protons and electrons coming toward our planet. How, then, did these great belts of radiation build up? The answer, made clear by many experiments both on earth and in satellites during the International Geophysical Year, is that the activity of the sun opens chinks in the earth's magnetic field, letting wandering particles enter occasionally.

"All but one little piece of the theory necessary for predicting the Van Allen belts was already available to scientists," says Lloyd Berkner. The only hole in existing knowledge was the erroneous assumption that the earth's magnetic field was constant.

"You have here the greatest of all reasons for experiment," Berkner declares. "Given the opportunity of making great theoretical discoveries, theoreticians didn't make them. . . . It's simply an illustration of the fact that you can't sit in a cell and do science, that science is fundamentally based on experiment, and the theory can only proceed when it goes hand in hand with the scientist's experiments."

Another good question is why the Van Allen belts were not discovered by the Russian scientists whose second satellite—Sputnik II—was equipped with the same kind of cosmic-ray counters and was launched almost three months previously, into the heart of the radiation zone. Soviet scientists told American colleagues later that they did obtain unexpectedly high readings.

But a set of readings from one satellite was not enough evidence on which to base a major discovery. Scientists everywhere in the world want to check and double-check their data before announcing results. The batteries aboard Sputnik II enabled its radio transmitter to remain in operation from November 3 to November 10, 1957. The obvious step was to launch another satellite with instruments designed to verify the previous results and to investigate other possibilities suggested by those results. However, it was not until the following May that they were able to induce the military authorities to launch another satellite.

The U.S. program, on the other hand, was conducted by scientists, with scientific objectives primarily in mind. Van Allen modified his Geiger counters to report a higher cosmic-ray count and the Army made an attempt to launch another satellite—Explorer II—less than five weeks after Explorer I. However, the fourth stage failed to ignite and orbit was not achieved. But the Army and Van Allen kept trying, and did succeed in putting the modified instruments into orbit as Explorer III on March 26. Explorer III carried a tiny tape recorder to obtain cosmic-ray information on the opposite side of the world, which was played back when it passed over a command station. The information, covering altitudes between the perigee of 117 miles and the apogee of 1741 miles, proved to Van Allen's satisfaction that the belt existed and he announced the discovery at a meeting of the National Academy of Sciences on May 1, 1958—two weeks before the Soviets launched Sputnik III.

Even before the announcement, word of the Van Allen findings spread among scientists and lent support to a bold, imaginative proposal made earlier by Nicholas C. Christofilos * of the Atomic Energy Commission's Lawrence Radiation Laboratory in Livermore, California. Christofilos was working on a project to make use of the thermonuclear reaction of the hydrogen bomb in a small machine designed to generate electrical power. The greatest problem in developing such a machine is to keep the protons (nuclei of hydrogen atoms) confined in a small space so as to light up the nuclear fusion reaction. Christofilos' approach was to trap the protons with a magnetic mirror.

Christofilos' study of the interaction of charged atomic particles and magnetic fields had led him to speculate, as several scientists had done before him, that the earth's magnetic field might create such a mirror in nearby space. A short time after the launching of the first Sputnik, Christofilos drew up a proposal to test the notion by exploding an atomic bomb in space, at a location where the earth's magnetic mirror might be found.

After Explorer I demonstrated the existence of a natural radiation belt, Christofilos' proposal won the support of the highest-ranking government scientists. Unlike the Explorer satellites, however, the experiment was not sponsored as part of the U.S. effort in the International Geophysical Year, all of which was conducted in public. Instead, the project, dubbed Project Argus, was carried out entirely in secret by the U.S. Department of Defense and its existence was not disclosed until the spring of 1959.

The Advanced Research Projects Agency, a Defense Department body just established for the task of supervising American space experiments, approved the project in April 1958. Herbert York, the youthful chief scientist of ARPA—now chancellor of

---

* Christofilos is the same "crazy Greek" who invented an improved method of focusing magnetic fields in an atomic-particle accelerator for the Atomic Energy Commission. A native of Boston who returned to Greece as a child, Christofilos learned engineering there and worked out the principle as a result of reading in his spare time. He wrote to the Radiation Laboratory of the University of California with the suggestion, but scientists there questioned his mathematics. Later, however, he read in a scientific journal that a plan similar to his was to be used in the design of a new accelerator at Brookhaven National Laboratory on Long Island. When Christofilos, then operating an elevator business in Athens, pointed out that he had applied for a patent on the idea, he was hired by the Atomic Energy Commission.

the San Diego campus of the University of California—organized a task force that obtained a ship, arranged for the launching of two satellites and more than a dozen sounding rockets, and carried out the experiment within a period of four months.

The U.S.S. *Norton Sound,* a guided-missile cruiser, was chosen for the job. Three nuclear fission bombs, of explosive yield between 5 per cent and 10 per cent of the bomb dropped on Hiroshima, were put on top of three-stage, solid-propelled X-17 rockets. A satellite, Explorer IV, was launched July 26, into an orbit with perigee of 157 miles and apogee of 1388 miles. The *Norton Sound* launched one bomb on August 27, another on August 30, both early in the morning, and the third a short time before midnight September 6. All were at an altitude of about 300 miles. The first was exploded at latitude 38°S, longitude 12°W, the second at 50°S, 8°W and the third at 50°S, 10°W.

Just as Christofilos had predicted, the electrons released by each bomb formed into a great arc, climbing from 300 miles to about 2500 miles near the equator and descending again to the edge of the atmosphere over the North Atlantic. Their collisions with the upper atmosphere created artificial auroras over the ship and at the opposite end of the arc in the North Atlantic. Explorer IV, which had been obtaining data on the normal levels of radiation for a month previously, recorded increases above the normal on 164 occasions between August 27 and September 21, which were attributed to the Argus explosions. Sputnik III also recorded the Argus effect. Another American rocket, Pioneer III, encountered what appeared to be a faint trace of Argus electrons on December 6. Then they faded out.

Meanwhile, the Air Force launched thirteen sounding rockets to altitudes ranging between 450 and 550 miles at Cape Canaveral, Wallops Island, Virginia, and Ramey Air Force Base, Puerto Rico, one on August 15 for basic radiation data and the others in the six days following the first explosion. The sounding rockets confirmed the satellite data. The only failure in the entire Argus operation was in the attempt to launch Explorer V on August 24. All stages fired properly but a collision between the first stage and the structure that carried the upper stages spoiled their aim. Happily however, Explorer IV continued transmitting. One of its two radios died September 9; the other October 6.

The ability of American scientists to follow up their experiments illustrates an apparent difference between the U.S. and Soviet approaches to space exploration. America's launchings were geared to science. In Russia, the experiments rode as passengers on rockets whose schedule was controlled by the military authorities. Soviet scientists merely designed the satellites and shipped them to the launching site. In early Sputnik launchings at least, Soviet scientists were not even present.

Explorer was not the only Amercian series of satellites to achieve early scientific success. The tiny $3\frac{1}{4}$-pound Vanguard produced a whole series of additions to man's knowledge. All depended on the technological feat of using the sun's light and heat to generate electric power in space. The first satellites—both Sputniks and Explorers—depended on batteries for electric power, just as does a flashlight. When the batteries ran down, the satellite radios stopped transmitting. No matter how long the satellites remained in orbit, they were almost useless after their batteries failed.

Vanguard, however, has a device called a solar cell, which produces a small electric current when the sun shines on it. The solar cell operates something like an automobile generator, charging the battery while in sunlight, and letting the radio transmitter draw on the battery while it is in the earth's shadow. One of Vanguard's two transmitters sends a signal on 108.03 megacycles with 0.005 watt of power drawn from a tiny battery. A second transmitter, powered by another battery, unconnected with the solar cell, ceased operating nineteen days after launch. Sputnik III, launched two months after Vanguard, also was powered by solar cells and its radios operated for twenty-three months.

Almost four years later, Vanguard was still transmitting and there was no indication it would stop for many years. The long life has made it possible to follow changes in the satellite's orbit with great precision and to draw many important scientific conclusions.

The first major result was a new measurement of the shape of the earth. Children are taught in elementary school that the earth is an oblate spheroid—almost perfectly round but with a shorter diameter from pole to pole than at the equator. Before Vanguard, geophysicists believed the oblateness to be 1/297. That fraction represents the difference between the diameter at the poles and that at the equator, divided by the average diameter. J. W. Siry, J. A. O'Keefe, Ann Eckels and R. K. Squires took Vanguard data, fed it into an electronic computer and obtained the fraction 1/298.2, which has since been confirmed by information from subsequent satellites. Thus, the earth is less oblate than had been previously believed.

Early study of Vanguard's orbit also showed that the atmosphere of the earth—rare as it is at altitudes above 400 miles—is nevertheless less rare than had been believed. Vanguard's orbit shrank faster than expected. The "atmosphere" at 400 miles is still a more perfect vacuum than it is possible to achieve on earth; however, Vanguard measurements indicated that it is about one ten-trillionth of the density of the air at sea level. This is about ten times as dense as had been predicted by the formulas in the "Air Research and Development Command Model Atmosphere," published in 1955.

Data from Vanguard orbits over a period of several months made possible more refined analysis of the earth's shape. A distortion was revealed. The assumption previous to Vanguard was that the northern and southern hemisphere are identical halves of a slightly flattened sphere. But Siry, Eckels, O'Keefe and Squires found instead that the southern hemisphere is a little more oblate—by about 100 feet. The sea level in the Arctic Ocean is 50 feet higher than had been considered normal, while at the south polar cap the level is 50 feet lower. Outside the polar caps, the sea level is about 25 feet lower in the northern hemisphere and about 25 feet higher in the southern hemisphere than would be the case if the oblate spheroid were perfectly symmetrical. The distorted shape indicates greater strength than had been believed to exist in the earth's mantle and crust. For if the rock were softer, the action of gravity would have brought about symmetry in the billions of years since the earth was formed.

Vanguard also confirmed many existing theories, including postulates that a satellite's orbit can be affected by the pressure of solar radiation, by the gravitational fields of the sun and moon, by a dragging force from the earth's magnetic field and by variations in "sunspot"—or solar storm—activity.

The long life of Vanguard might appear to give grounds for hope of confirming Albert Einstein's general theory of relativity —which holds, among other things, that light rays are bent by gravitational force. One of the few pieces of evidence available in support of the general theory is a slow, otherwise unexplainable rotation of the nearest point to the sun of the orbit of the planet Mercury. The relativity theory predicts that such rotation takes place to a measurable extent only very close to the central body. Thus Mercury, the closest planet to the Sun, is the only one for which any change is observed.

An artificial satellite, much closer to the Earth than Mercury is to the Sun, could be expected to show a relativistic change in its orbit, which ought to become apparent if it is tracked closely for a year or two. However, air drag and other effects on the Vanguard orbit are so much greater that they mask the relativistic effect. Apparently, it will be necessary to launch a small, long-lived satellite into a much higher orbit—perhaps with an altitude of 1000 to 2000 miles—to verify the Einstein effect.

The early satellites were followed by larger and more spectacular accomplishments by the Soviets and by American attempts to get the greatest performance from our smaller rockets. The third Sputnik, launched May 15, 1958, carried 2925 pounds of scientific instruments to an orbit with apogee of 1167 miles and perigee of 135 miles. Sputnik III provided a wealth of data on the Van Allen belts and confirmed a long-held theory that there is a "ring current" circling the earth high above the equator. Sputnik III also carried experiments to measure atmospheric pressure and composition, concentration of positive ions, magnetic fields, the earth's electrical field, micrometeors and temperatures, as well as cosmic rays. Its radios continued operating until April 6, 1960.

Despite the good scientific results attained by U.S. satellites, American rocket technology was in a miserable condition. The Navy's successful launching of Vanguard I, coming after two failures, was followed by four more failures later in 1958. Here is a chronological catalogue of the causes: "malfunction in the first stage," "flight connection between units of first stage control system failed," "two minor components malfunctioned and failed to signal third stage to fire," "second stage engine failed to cut off properly," "second stage motor cut off prematurely due to low chamber pressure," "second stage failed to provide enough velocity."

The Army's Jupiter-C started well but ended the year with a mixed record. In six attempts to launch satellites, three were successful. By summer, a third service, the Air Force, had entered the picture with a rocket of its own, first called Project Able. The new Air Force rocket used a Thor intermediate-range ballistic missile (IRBM) as its first stage. Thus the new rocket soon became known as Thor-Able. The Air Force adapted the second stage of Vanguard for use atop the Thor and made use of a new third stage, originally developed for Vanguard, but used for the first time with Thor-Able.

The new third-stage rocket—called X-248—made use of an interesting method of saving weight. The original third stage produced for Vanguard had a steel chamber, as did most solid-propellant rockets of the time. The internal burning of solid rockets develops a very high pressure. Thus great strength is required. The new rocket saved weight by using thousands of miles of fiber glass wound around a mold and glued together with plastic. Every pound saved in the weight of the final stage of a rocket makes it possible to add a pound of payload. Thus the substitution—together with an improved rocket fuel—greatly increased the payload capacity. For comparison, Vanguard II, with the old third stage, boosted a satellite weighing 20.7 pounds into orbit. Vanguard III, with the fiber glass-plastic rocket, carried 50 pounds of instruments.

On its first launching, however, the brand new plastic rocket never had a chance to be tested. The Thor first stage blew up 77 seconds after launch. The occasion, on August 17, 1958, was America's first attempt at shooting a spacecraft to the environs of the moon. The greater power of the Thor, substituted for the smaller Vanguard first stage, made it possible to attempt trajectories leading to escape from the earth's gravitational field. Vanguard and Jupiter-C had enough power to accelerate a small satellite to the speed of 25,900 feet per second (17,100 miles per hour) required to attain orbit. But escape from earth requires a velocity of more than 36,000 feet per second (about 25,000 miles per hour)—more than 40 per cent higher.

Thor-Able was launched a second time toward the moon on October 11. This time, all three stages fired properly, but a tiny error in the angle at which the third stage was pointed prevented the 84.4 pound spacecraft—named Pioneer I—from attaining escape velocity. After climbing to an altitude of 70,700 statute miles, it plunged back into the South Pacific the following day. A third Thor-Able was launched November 8. This time, the first two stages burned properly, but the third stage did not ignite. The November rocket, named Pioneer II, climbed to 963 miles before falling back.

Next, it was the Army's turn to shoot for the moon. Von Braun's group also took an IRBM—the Jupiter—and substituted it for the Redstone first stage in their earlier rocket assembly, the Jupiter-C.* The three solid-propellant upper stages remained the same. The bigger first stage made it possible to lift payloads of about 90 pounds on orbital missions, compared with a maximum of 38.4 pounds for Jupiter-C.

The new moon rocket was named Juno II. The first one, launched on December 6, 1958, carried a cone-shaped spacecraft with length of 23 inches and maximum diameter of 10 inches to a peak altitude of 63,580 miles. Although it weighed only 12.95 pounds, the tiny craft, named Pioneer III, carried two Geiger counters to measure cosmic rays, a photoelectric device to obtain a crude image of the back of the moon and battery-powered radios. Like Pioneer I, the rocket stages on Pioneer III fired properly but a slight error in the angle of the final stage prevented achievement of escape velocity.

Another important experiment during the same period was Project Score, in which the Air Force launched an entire Atlas intercontinental ballistic missile (ICBM) into orbit December 18, carrying 150 pounds of communication equipment. A Christmas message from President Eisenhower, recorded and retransmitted from space on command from the ground, demonstrated the feasibility of using satellites for communications. And, since the entire shell of the Atlas remained attached to the payload, the total weight of 8750 pounds qualified it as the heaviest U.S. satellite. It could not be compared, of course, to Sputnik III, whose total payload was 2925 pounds, almost twenty times the weight of instruments in Score, although the final rocket stage that followed the Soviet satellite into orbit weighed only about 4000 pounds.

After four widely publicized failures by the United States, Russia succeeded in launching the first object propelled by man beyond the pull of the earth's gravity. On January 2, 1959, a spacecraft named Mechta (Russian for dream) weighing 3245 pounds left the earth, passed within 4700 miles of the moon and

* The name Jupiter-C is somewhat confusing because the Jupiter IRBM was not a part of the assembly. Later, the name was officially changed to Juno I. Unofficially, however, the name Jupiter-C remained.

went into orbit about the sun as an artificial planetoid. Mechta —called Lunik in the West—carried instruments to measure interplanetary gas, solar radiation, magnetic fields of the earth and moon, meteoritic matter and cosmic radiation. It also generated a yellow cloud by releasing sodium gas in space a short time after launching. Soviet scientists said they received signals from Lunik to a distance of 400,000 miles, about 160,000 miles beyond the moon.

The Soviet achievement took most of the edge off America's success two months later. An Army Juno II launched a 13.4-pound cone—named Pioneer IV—which came within 37,300 miles of the moon and entered a similar solar orbit. It did not pass close enough—within 20,000 miles was necessary—to operate the photoelectric sensor. However, radio contact was maintained and cosmic rays were counted out to a distance of 407,000 miles.

Thus, by the end of the International Geophysical Year, the United States had achieved notable successes in scientific discovery. But the Soviet Union had won most of the points in propaganda. There was almost unanimous agreement that America would have to devote more effort—and spend more money—to do a more thorough job of exploring space.

5. MAN IN SPACE

ALTHOUGH SPACE AND MISSILES produced considerable controversy in Congress and its committees during 1958—an election year—there was general agreement on two points, that a new civilian space agency should be established and that manned flight in space should be a major national objective.

There were three primary reasons for setting up a new civilian agency. First was a general lack of confidence in the ability of the military services to manage an activity that involved civilian industry. The successful operation of the War Production Board by civilians in World War II was contrasted with the confusion and jurisdictional squabbling that attended the missile programs run by the military services in the late 1950s. The latter situation, of course, was a direct result of the organization of the Department of Defense. The 1947 law that established the Air Force as a third branch of the services, and Defense as a supervisor of the three, was a compromise between true unification and none at all. In practical effect, the Defense Department had become a new layer in the hierarchy, many of whose officials had veto power without responsibility, power to say no but not to enforce affirmative action. In areas where Defense had operating responsibility, it often became in effect a fourth branch, competing with the other three. There was widespread opinion that a civilian agency, with a single executive, could move faster and more efficiently.

The second reason was emphasis. The military services are in the business of national defense. When developing a program and parceling out the available funds, they have to give priority to projects with a direct defense application. All three services have given support to basic scientific research. But space exploration requires hardware whose cost is much greater than most research. As a result, it tends to fall to the bottom of the defense priority list. A separate agency, clearly charged with exploring space, would have a better chance of winning funds and priority.

The third reason was the effect on world opinion. If the United States is to engage in space activity for reasons of prestige and propaganda, it was argued, conduct by a civilian agency will emphasize the nation's peaceful intentions. In a message to Congress April 2, 1958, recommending establishment of the new agency, President Eisenhower expressed it this way: ". . . A civilian setting for the administration of space function will emphasize the concern of our nation that outer space be devoted to peaceful and scientific purposes."

The three arguments weighed heavily with both the Republican administration and the Democratic majorities in Congress. A fourth consideration also influenced Congress. Creating a new permanent agency would make it possible to establish new permanent committees in both houses. Two new chairmanships and some patronage would be available. Setting up a new agency would take time, however, and the nation was clamoring for action. And so, early in February, a rider to an appropriation bill authorized the Defense Department to establish an Advanced Research Projects Agency with authority to conduct a national space program for one year.

Many officers of the military services, particularly in the research branches, would have preferred that the Defense Department have permanent charge of all space activity. But there would have been continued wrangling about roles and missions —who would do what—which was just what the sponsors of the civilian agency wanted to avoid. Eisenhower assigned the job of drawing up the bill to his new special assistant for science and technology, President James R. Killian of Massachusetts Institute of Technology, and the Bureau of the Budget. They obtained agreement from top Defense officials to the idea of a civilian agency. The speed with which the legislation was rushed through the Pentagon suggests that the sponsors wished to present the military hierarchy with a fait accompli. In any case, the military had to go along with their civilian superiors.

The new space agency was to be built around the National Advisory Committee for Aeronautics, a forty-three-year-old aeronautical research organization with a staff of 8000, which had a reputation of high technical competence. The NACA had worked for many years with the military services in developing new aircraft. Since World War II, it had become increasingly active in rocket research, and operated a rocket test station at Wallops Island in the Atlantic Ocean, off the eastern shore of Virginia. The NACA had lived a quiet life, insulated to some extent from Washington agency rivalry by its committee management and by the fact that it did not contract with private industry for the development of hardware. On January 27, 1958, Hugh L. Dryden, NACA Director, proposed in a speech before a scientific organization that the same division of functions be continued for space exploration development—NACA to perform the government research and provide technical assistance, and the military services to contract for hardware development. But the administration bill gave the new agency contracting authority as well.

The idea of manned space flight won approval with scarcely any more debate than was occasioned by the idea of establishing a civilian agency. Only a few scientists expressed doubts in their testimony before the Congressional committees. One was H. Guyford Stever, Associate Dean of Engineering at M.I.T., Chairman of a committee advising the NACA. "We still have a question as to the reason for a man in space," he said. Lee A. DuBridge, president of California Institute of Technology, raised the question in these terms:

"Is it simply to give him a ride for the sake of the stunt, the adventure? If so, let's be honest about that and then we can decide how much such an adventure is worth to the taxpayers." If the purpose is to operate scientific instruments or to make scientific observations, he maintained, "we must ask whether unmanned scientific instruments could do the job as well for less cost. And in many cases it will be found that a man contributes nothing or very little to what could be done with instruments alone."

Hugh Odishaw, Executive Director of the U.S. National Committee for the International Geophysical Year, replied to this question in a report to the National Academy of Sciences. He said:

"The attainment of manned space flight cannot now be very clearly justified on purely rational grounds. It is possible, at least in principle, to design equipment which will do all the sensing needed to explore space and the planets. Mobile vehicles could be designed to land and crawl across the face of each of these distant worlds, measuring, touching, looking, listening, and reporting back to earth all the impressions gained. They could be remotely controlled and so could act like hands, eyes, and ears for the operator on earth. Moreover, such robots could be abandoned without qualm when they ran out of fuel or broke down.

"Though all this could be done in principle, there may be a point at which the complexity of the machine to do the job becomes intolerable, and a man is found to be more efficient, more reliable, and above all, more resourceful when unexpected obstacles arise. It is, in a sense, an article of faith that man will indeed be required to do the job of cosmic exploration personally and, furthermore, that he will want to do the job himself, whether required to or not."

The "article of faith" carried the day. The only real controversy was about Wernher von Braun's proposal that a Redstone rocket be used to launch a manned capsule 150 miles into space on a ballistic flight. His idea was that, with an existing rocket, it would be possible to achieve a brief manned space flight very quickly, perhaps within a year, and thus score a first for the United States. The von Braun proposal, called Project Adam, was approved by the Army and the Department of Defense, but was rejected by the Operations Coordinating Board, a White House body, because of the objections of scientists. Director Dryden of the NACA voiced the prevalent scientific opinion in testimony before a House committee on April 16, 1958. He said such a flight would have "the same technical value as the circus stunt of shooting the young lady from the gun." He won quick agreement from Major General Bernard A. Schriever, commander of the Air Force Ballistic Missile Division, and Arthur Kantrowitz, Research Director of the Avco Corporation. Schriever voiced preference for a program of orbiting animals, developing a recovery technique and then going on to manned flight in orbit—something that could be accomplished with the Air Force

intercontinental missiles, Atlas and Titan. Kantrowitz said the
only information gained would be what happens to a man during a few minutes of weightlessness. "This is another project
which is off the main track," Kantrowitz asserted, "because I feel
that weightlessness is not a major problem."

The Army leaped to von Braun's support. Major General J. B.
Medaris, commander of the Army Ordnance Missile Command,
called the Redstone project "a necessary and essential prereq-
uisite to the careful step-by-step advance of our ability to transport people by missile." Retired Lieutenant General James M.
Gavin, former Army research chief, asserted: "We have to walk
before we run. The problems of housing a man through this
experience, as brief as it may be, will contribute in the long
run to using manned missiles."

Thus the dispute, like so many controversies about missiles,
reduced itself to competition between two military services for
funds. In this case, scientists supported the Air Force and its
views prevailed with the Eisenhower administration. But to the
leaders of the Democratic majority in Congress, von Braun was
the man of the hour. The same Redstone had constituted the
first stage of the Jupiter-C rocket that had launched America's
first satellite less than three months previously. Von Braun had
told Congress he could have launched a satellite more than a
year ahead of the Soviet Sputnik, had he been allowed. The
Congressional Democrats made it clear to the administration
that they had no intention of allowing von Braun's proposal to
be shut out of the man-in-space program.

As a result of the controversy, Dryden amended his statement.
On April 22, he told the House Select Committee on Astronautics and Space Exploration: "This simple experiment standing
alone as an objective, to me is not of very much greater value
than the shooting of a young lady from a cannon. It does give
you a little scientific information at a great deal of cost. It may
be justified as part of a very comprehensive program." Thus he
prepared the way for a program that would include both the
Army Redstone and the Air Force ICBM.

While Congress was considering the legislation, technical staffs
of NACA and Air Force contractors worked on plans for the
manned orbital flight. Both came to the conclusion that model
D of the Atlas was the rocket to be assigned the propulsion job.
The Atlas is the smaller of the two intercontinental missiles,

with a capacity to carry 2500 pounds into orbit, compared with about 3000 pounds for the Titan. There are two basic differences between the two missiles, both of which use liquid fuel. The Atlas is a "one-and-a-half-stage" missile. It has three rockets * that ignite on the ground. After two minutes of flight, two large engines fall away and the missile continues on its way, powered by a single engine of lesser power. Titan, on the other hand, is a two-stage missile. Not only the engines, but the entire first stage, including fuel tanks, falls away when the engines stop burning. The other difference is in construction. Atlas has a thin skin of stainless steel, whose stiffness is maintained by the pressure of gas in the tanks. Titan uses aluminum of greater structural strength. Thus it can be seen that there are technical reasons for preferring Titan.

But the Atlas had been under development with full funding and priority for more than a year longer than the Titan and was that much nearer readiness. Both the Air Force and NACA studies concluded that time would be lost by waiting for Titan. Robert R. Gilruth of the government research agency also saw a reliability advantage in the fact that all three Atlas rockets are lighted on the ground. "In Titan," he said in 1961, "you are involved with the ignition of a second stage, which is perhaps a small point as the reliability of these devices gets better and better but it is probably still a fairly important point in today's technology."

In the Air Force, the Ballistic Missile Division and the development center at Wright Field worked out eight successive plans for manned orbital flight before gaining the approval of the new Defense Department research agency. It exchanged views with the scientists and engineers of NACA, but there were a number of technical differences between the two designs developed. After receiving a series of industrial design studies earlier in the year, the Air Force began a competition in June for the study and final design of a space cabin and internal systems for support of an astronaut. The stage of awarding the contract was reached, but the contract was not awarded. For in August, with the pas-

* All told, the Atlas actually has five rocket engines. The large engines of the booster have 150,000 or 165,000 pounds thrust each. The smaller sustainer engine generates 60,000 pounds. In addition are two small "vernier" engines of 1000 pounds thrust apiece, which give final course correction after the sustainer burns out.

sage of the Space Act of 1958, the job of choosing a contractor
to develop the hardware was assigned to the new agency, the
National Aeronautics and Space Administration. The results of
the Air Force competition were transferred to NASA. "We were
just told to pick up our marbles and go home," remarked a bitter Air Force officer. Some of the industrial companies were
equally bitter when the new agency started the competition all
over again.

President Eisenhower appointed T. Keith Glennan, president
of Case Institute of Technology, Cleveland, as administrator of
the space agency. Dryden was named as his deputy. On October
7, 1958, six days after NASA went into operation, a Space Task
Group was formed at Langley Field, near Norfolk, Virginia, lo-
cale of an NASA research center. Robert R. Gilruth of the Langley Center became director of the task group and of the manned
flight program, later named Project Mercury. At NASA headquarters in Washington, Glennan appointed Abe Silverstein of
the NACA Lewis Research Center in Cleveland as director of
space development. Silverstein established an office of manned
space flight under the direction of George M. Low, also from
the Lewis Center.

A joint panel of the new NASA and the Defense Department
worked out plans for cooperation in carrying out Project Mercury. The civilian agency would need considerable operational
support from the military services.

The first question to be settled was the shape of the spacecraft.
Two possibilities were considered, a teardrop shape like the nose
cone of a ballistic missile, and a shape with wings. The teardrop
would depend on the dragging effect of the atmosphere to slow
it down after it re-entered; it would require parachutes for
landing. A winged craft would glide to a chosen point. There
were obvious advantages in a shape that permitted controlled
flight in the atmosphere. But there were two disadvantages. First,
the winged craft would have to be heavier, perhaps by 30 or 40
per cent. The additional weight increased the payload requirement beyond the capability of the Atlas D. The second was that
a winged vehicle would require more time. "I think you will
find a very general agreement among all contractors who studied
it," Dryden said, "that the quickest way to get a man into space
is through the use of the so-called drag-type vehicle, that it
would take much longer to develop a winged vehicle." In some

of the studies for the Air Force, additional rocket stages above the Atlas were proposed with the idea of increasing the weight capacity. However, the civilian agency rejected any such plan on the grounds that developing a new rocket would cause delay and unreliability.

The joint NASA-military panel approved a program for Project Mercury consisting of three phases: ballistic flights of about 300 miles boosted by a Redstone rocket, flights up to 1500 miles with the Army Jupiter and flights into orbit and return with the Air Force Atlas D. However, the Jupiter flights were dropped from the program in mid-1959. The objective of all the flights would be to evaluate man's capabilities in a space environment and to perfect hardware and equipment to support him.

A fundamental requirement was a foolproof escape device, in the event of rocket failure. "I think we must recognize," George Low said, "that the Atlas vehicle itself will not be completely reliable by the time period that we will be launching it." Low, a Viennese who had fled Austria as a boy in 1940, promised that the escape system woud be "as nearly completely reliable as any system has ever been. . . . We will not send a man on the Mercury mission until we are convinced that it will be no more dangerous than a normal test flying type operation."

Choosing astronauts was an early problem. A selection group, composed of the project technical chiefs and a committee of air —medical advisers,* established five basic requirements: graduation from a military test-pilot school; 1500 hours of flying experience; bachelor degree or equivalent in engineering or science; age under 40; and height of 5 feet 11 inches or less. "In many ways," Low said, "the type of decisions and the physical and mental stresses involved are similar to those that confront an experimental test pilot."

A group of 110 pilots chosen from the services met the preliminary requirements. After further study of individual records, the group was reduced to sixty-nine, all of whom were invited

---

* Members were Doctor W. Randolph Lovelace, Albuquerque, New Mexico, chairman; Captain Norman L. Barr, USN; Lieutenant Commander John H. Ebersole, USN; Brigadier General Donald D. Flickinger, USAF; Lieutenant Colonel Robert H. Holmes, USA; Doctor Wright H. Langham, Los Alamos, New Mexico; Doctor Robert B. Livingston, Bethesda, Maryland; Doctor Orr Reynolds, Washington, D.C.; and Boyd C. Myers II of NASA, secretary.

to volunteer. Of these, fifty-five accepted the invitation and went through a series of interviews and examinations of their physical and psychological condition and response to stress.

What manner of men were the volunteers? "One might expect strong intimations of psychopathology," remarked George E. Ruff and Edwin Z. Levy, two Air Force medical officers who conducted the psychiatric evaluations. "The high incidence of emotional disorders in volunteers for laboratory experiments had much to do with the decision to consider only candidates with records of effective performance under difficult circumstances in the past."

The psychiatrists were surprised, however, to find the volunteers quite normal. "There was no evidence for a diagnosis of psychosis, significant neurosis or personality disorder in a single member of the group." Of the thirty-one men who went through the full selection procedure, the average age was thirty-three, with a range from twenty-seven to thirty-eight. All but one was married. All but two grew up in small towns. Twenty of them were only sons or the oldest of the children in their families.

"These were comfortable, mature, well-integrated individuals," the psychiatrists found. "Most were direct action-oriented individuals, who spent little time introspecting. Although dependency needs were not overly strong, most showed the capacity to relate effectively to other people."

One theory of psychiatry holds that great interest in high-performance aircraft can be related to feelings of inadequacy in sexual areas. Ruff and Levy made a thorough review of each candidate's adolescence, but they could uncover little information to bear out the theory. "A high proportion of these men apparently passed through adolescence in comfortable fashion. Most made excellent school and social adjustments. Many had been class presidents or showed other evidence of leadership."

The psychiatrists sought to make generalizations about the men's motives in volunteering. They varied widely, but most were a mixture of professionalism, love of adventure and the opportunity to advance their careers. One commented, "There aren't many new frontiers. This is a chance to be in on one of them." Another said it would be "a chance to get in on the ground floor of the biggest thing man has ever done." A third said space travel would be "the next big step in aviation."

The average intelligence quotient of the thirty-one men tested was 133, which is higher than ninety-eight per cent of the people of the United States. The seven who were finally selected scored a little higher still, in a range from 130 to 141, with an average of 135. The choices, announced April 9, 1959, were:

John H. Glenn Jr., lieutenant colonel, Marine Corps, age 37.
Walter M. Schirra Jr., lieutenant commander, Navy, 36.
Alan B. Shepard Jr., lieutenant commander, Navy, 35.
Donald K. Slayton, captain, Air Force, 35.
Malcolm S. Carpenter, lieutenant, Navy, 33.
Virgil I. Grissom, captain, Air Force, 33.
Leroy G. Cooper Jr., captain, Air Force, 32.

Thus the seven pilots consisted of three from the Air Force, three from the Navy and one from the Marine Corps. All were detailed to the space administration, but retained their rank, service pay and chances for promotion. All seven were married and fathers of children. All were Protestant.

Meanwhile, NASA had chosen the McDonnell Aircraft Corporation of St. Louis, Missouri, as the prime contractor to develop the space capsule. Although the Air Force had carried the selection process to the choice of two final competitors, neither of which was McDonnell, the civilian agency had decided to begin again, because its specifications were different from those of the Air Force. However, very little time was lost in the process. NASA chose McDonnell on January 12, 1959, just three months after the formation of its task group.

Project Mercury, by far the most widely publicized phase of the U.S. space program, was nevertheless not a complete success in the realm of public relations. During the two years between the selection of the astronauts and the first suborbital flight, the program was involved in frequent controversy.

The first dispute raged after the disclosure that the seven astronauts had sold their personal stories to *Life* Magazine. The contract, on a collective basis, is reported to call for payment of a half-million dollars. Regardless of legality or propriety, it was a major blunder in relations with the press. Although the project gained the benefit of regular publicity for the astronauts in one magazine, the contract had the effect of discouraging favorable publicity elsewhere. Magazine and newspaper editors, who are subject to the same frailties as the rest of the human race, often took the attitude that a favorable story about Project

Mercury would have the effect of advertising a regular offering of an opposing publication. As a result, the majority of popular magazines ignored the subject of man in space except for an occasional critical article.

In a less publicized but no less important sphere was the civilian agency's method of dealing with industry. The Air Force, with a relatively small staff of technical specialists, has tended to give its contractors considerable technical freedom, which has naturally pleased the contractors. The NASA, however, has a very large staff of technical specialists, who scrutinized the contractor's work in great detail and did much of the basic design work "in house," leaving the contractors only the assignment to carry out instructions. The industrial contractors, many of whom worked on both Air Force and space agency projects, generally lobbied on behalf of the Air Force, for which they preferred to work.

A third problem was the understandable unwillingness of Eisenhower administration officials to concede publicly that the United States was in a race with Russia to achieve the first manned flight, although most privately recognized it. Administrator Glennan would not even make the admission in the privacy of staff meetings. The reason for the unwillingness was simple. Russia had orbited a dog in November, 1957, a year before the formation of Project Mercury, and had launched animals and recovered them alive from ballistic flights in space by the summer of 1958. The Russian lead was so great that the race would be impossible to win. The dates by which specific test flights and other milestones were to be accomplished were supposed to be kept confidential, on the ground that they were merely targets established to insure that contractors deliver parts and components on time. Nevertheless, the target dates became known and the agency was criticized in the trade press—which reflected the views of the aircraft industry—for failing to meet them.

Project Mercury encountered a good share of technical difficulties. It isn't possible to compare the problems with those of the missile programs because many of the details of the military programs are secret. Project Mercury has been carried out under an injunction to NASA in the Space Act of 1958 to "provide for the widest practicable and appropriate dissemination of information concerning its activities and the results thereof." Here are some of the things that went wrong under the pitiless glare of publicity:

On July 29, 1960, after takeoff in a driving rain from Cape Canaveral, an Atlas with a Mercury capsule aboard exploded at an altitude of about 40,000 feet. The cause was never established for certain, although the consensus of the engineers put the finger on weakness at the front end of the Atlas tanks, designed to carry a warhead much less bulky than the Mercury capsule. The explosion, sixty-five seconds after liftoff, took place at the moment when the pressure caused by the air was highest —called "max Q" by the engineers. It caused a seven-month delay in the Mercury Atlas test program, while the cause was sought. On the next flight, February 21, 1961, an eight-inch-wide steel band, designed by Abe Silverstein, was added to strengthen the front end. The crew in the blockhouse cheered lustily when the missile passed safely through max Q.

On November 8, 1960, the day millions of Americans voted by a narrow margin to elect John F. Kennedy as President, the capsule escape system failed to operate properly in a test flight from Wallops Island, Virginia. The escape system uses a powerful solid-fuel rocket, designed to pull the capsule away from its Redstone or Atlas booster at the first indication of any sort of trouble. In this case, the escape rocket fired prematurely, before the capsule and the booster rocket separated.

An electrical wire a few inches too short caused an even more embarrassing failure less than two weeks later, on November 21. A stray current lasting a tiny fraction of a second, caused when one wire disconnected too soon, shut down a Redstone missile at the moment it left the launch pad. As a result, the missile settled back on its haunches and the escape tower jettisoned itself, landing in a sand and palmetto area 1200 feet away. The parachutes unfurled and then drooped lazily over the rocket and spacecraft. Since all connections with the missile had been severed, it was impossible to remove the fuel and liquid oxygen by remote control. Engineers waited two days for the liquid oxygen to boil away before it was safe to approach the missile. Four weeks later, on December 19, the situation was made right by making one wire longer than the other, so that plugs would disconnect in the proper sequence.

Further difficulty developed with the Redstone on the second flight in the Mercury series—designated MR-2—in which a chimpanzee named Ham tested the capsule life-support system. The Redstone engine developed excessive fuel consumption and thrust, so that the tanks emptied a few seconds ahead of schedule. The earlier than normal shutdown gave a signal for the firing of the escape rocket, sending the unfortunate animal 100 miles beyond the farthest of the waiting ships. The capsule was damaged by the impact and water leaked in during the two hours it lay on its side before recovery by helicopter. The chimpanzee barely escaped drowning. The engineers also confirmed a previous indication of control system vibration in the Redstone. As a result, von Braun recommended another Redstone flight before risking a man's life. The additional flight, which took place March 24, 1961, was successful.

The Atlas ran into more trouble on its third attempt to boost a Mercury capsule, on April 25, 1961. This time, more than the usual press, television and radio complement was present. The extras were early arrivals for the first manned Redstone flight scheduled for the following week. For its first forty seconds of flight, the Atlas climbed straight up, instead of tilting eastward according to its program, and the range safety officer pressed the "destruct" button. The test was doubly disappointing because, had it continued another half minute, it would have reached the "max Q" region and provided another test of the front end strengthening.

Before it took office, the Kennedy administration took a jaundiced view of Project Mercury. On January 12, 1961, an "Ad Hoc Committee on Space" reported to the President-elect that the Atlas as a booster for Mercury orbital flight is "marginal." The committee, headed by Jerome B. Wiesner, who was to be Kennedy's scientific adviser, questioned the placing of the highest national priority on the project. The committee declared that the priority had "strengthened the popular belief that man in space is the most important aim of our non-military space effort. . . . It exaggerates the value of that aspect of space activity where we are less likely to achieve success, and discounts those aspects in which we have already achieved great success and will probably reap further successes in the future."

6. GAGARIN

EAST OF THE ARAL SEA, in a region northwest of the ancient city of Tashkent, is a wide desert, the Kara-Kumy Sands, with a smaller extension to the eastward, the Mayun-Kumy sands. Midway in the Mayun-Kumy sands, about 100 miles southwest of the town of Baikonur, is an oasis called Kara-Kul-Bulak.

Until about fifteen years ago, the desert was populated only by Kazak nomads, best known to the world as the namesakes of the fearless cavalrymen of the Russian czarist armies. But great steel towers now rise from the desert near Kara-Kul-Bulak. And a city has sprung up to the southwest, near the rail station Tyura-Tam, to become one of the world's great centers of science and technology. Just how large a city now stands there is a Soviet state secret.

A short time after sunrise on April 12, 1961, a twenty-seven-year-old Red Air Force officer climbed fourteen steps up a steel gangway to a platform at the base of one of the tallest of the steel towers near Kara-Kul-Bulak. He turned and waved to several dozen men standing below. And then Major Yuri Alexeyevich Gagarin stepped into an elevator that carried him to a level about 125 feet above the ground, where he was helped into Vostok (East), a vehicle resting atop a giant two-stage rocket.

About four hours later, at 11:07 A.M., local time, the rocket lifted, climbed straight upward for about a half minute and then arched over to the northeast. When the second stage burned out and fell away about five minutes later, Gagarin had become the first human to leave this planet. The flight carried him the length of Siberia, over Omsk, Tomsk and Yakutsk before he passed out over the Pacific Ocean, curved southeastward and swung around Cape Horn at the southern tip of South America before turning to the northeast again across the Atlantic Ocean and Africa. While he was over Africa, a retro rocket fired, reducing the Vostok's speed enough so that gravity pulled it back through the atmosphere. Thirty minutes later, the spacecraft landed by parachute near the village of Smelkova, east of the Volga River, about fifteen miles south of the city of Saratov in European Russia.

Gagarin's flight was the occasion for a great national celebration. In a telephone conversation with the pilot, Nikita Khrushchev exulted, "Let the capitalist countries catch up with our country!" Two days later, the Premier greeted the cosmonaut at Moscow's Vnukovo Airport and the two led a motorcade to Red Square. Thousands lined the twenty-one miles of road; tens of thousands massed in Red Square to see Gagarin honored with the titles of Hero of the Soviet Union and Pilot Cosmonaut of the USSR. The Premier declared in his speech that Gagarin's flight showed that "Socialism has thrown open to our country boundless scope for development."

"In forty-three years of Soviet government," Khrushchev continued, "formerly illiterate Russia, of which some people spoke disparagingly, regarding it as a barbaric nation, has traveled a magnificent road. . . . This victory is another triumph of Lenin's idea, confirmation of the correctness of the Marxist-Leninist teaching. . . . This exploit marks a new upsurge of our nation in its onward movement towards communism."

In the months that followed, Gagarin toured the world to help the Soviet Union gain propaganda advantage from his accomplishment. One of his most successful visits was to Britain, where he was wildly acclaimed by the public and had lunch with Queen Elizabeth II at Buckingham Palace—although the British government had not invited him.

How did "formerly illiterate Russia" accomplish this great technological feat? At first, we should recall that a Russian, Konstantin Eduardovich Tsiolkovsky, originated many of the modern ideas about rockets and space flight at the turn of the century, and that construction of experimental rockets began in the Soviet Union as early as 1929, about the same time that Robert

Goddard moved to New Mexico. In 1934, the Soviet government began a large rocket program aimed at capitalizing on the rocket's military potential. The Red Army used small rockets widely during World War II.

At the end of the war, the Red Army occupied Peenemuende and captured many of the German test and production engineers. Thus Russia had access to the same information and technical know-how from Peenemuende as did the West. Most of the Germans remained as prisoners until about 1952, but a group of electronic experts were held until 1958. Russia did not put the Germans to work at the Russian rocket centers. Instead, they were questioned endlessly at their prison camps, until they had been drained of useful information.

After the Germans returned home, they reported that they had not been used by Russia. As a result, the impression developed in some quarters that Russia did not have a large rocket development program. Wernher von Braun, in the United States, made a public statement in 1955 that the Soviet missile program was confused and poorly administered. Later that year, however, von Braun gained United States citizenship and obtained access to U.S. intelligence information. It then became clear, von Braun said, "that there existed an entirely independent Soviet Russian ballistic missile development program of which the German scientists taken into Soviet Russia were not even aware." He told a Congressional committee the probable contribution of German scientists to the Sputnik program was very little.

Russian scientists improved the German V-2 rocket engine, increasing its thrust from 55,000 to 77,000 pounds, about the same degree of improvement it gained in the United States to become the Redstone. But they also began work a short time after the war on a rocket four times as powerful as the V-2, with a thrust of 220,000 pounds (100 metric tons). This rocket engine, designated the R-14, became the basic unit of the T-3 intercontinental ballistic missile and all of Russia's early space efforts. Later in the game, the R-14 was improved to increase its thrust to 264,000 pounds; the improved engine was designated R-14A. Its fuels were liquid oxygen and a petroleum derivative similar to kerosene—just as in the modern American rockets.

Soon after Russia exploded her first nuclear bomb in 1949, Stalin ordered the beginning of work on a rocket big enough to deliver it against targets in the United States. I have no pipe-line to the heart of the Soviet missile effort, and so I cannot say just what successive designs were considered and rejected in the eight years between 1949 and 1957. However, it is clear that the first Soviet bomb was a bulky, crude affair, requiring tre-mendous thrust in the takeoff rocket. At the very least, the first stage would have had to have two R-14A engines, with total thrust of 530,000 pounds. It is possible three or four such en-gines might have been required. However, the weight of the warhead was reduced to the point at which only two R-14 en-gines were required in the first ICBM, the T-3. Thus Russia, by 1957, was in the happy position of having developed in the R-14A a rocket engine more powerful than actually required for an ICBM.

To launch Sputnik I, Soviet scientists merely added a small third stage to the T-3. Even with the smaller of their two booster rockets, they were able to launch in orbit a satellite weighing 184 pounds, almost ten times that of America's Vanguard and Explorer satellites, still to be launched. But they moved over to the more powerful R-14A booster for the heavier payload of Sputnik II, which carried a dog passenger. The Sputnik II pay-load weighed 1120 pounds, but that was far from the ultimate capacity of the new rocket vehicle. On May 15, 1958, Russia launched Sputnik III, a scientific satellite, weighing 2925 pounds.

Thus, Soviet scientists were able to capitalize on designing their rocket engines with margin for error. They built a rocket bigger than eventually proved necessary for the missile assign-ment but were able to use it for launching huge satellites, even at the very beginning of their efforts in space. In the United States, however, work on large rockets did not begin in earnest until 1954, when a breakthrough in hydrogen bomb develop-ment made it possible to make them much smaller and lighter than before. And then, the American rocket was built just barely large enough. The standard American rocket generates a thrust of 150,000 pounds. Recently, however, two improved versions of this rocket, of 165,000 and 188,000 pounds thrust have been developed.

"Formerly illiterate Russia" began just as early to learn about the ability of living things to withstand conditions in outer space. Russian scientists began launching dogs to altitudes up to 60 miles in 1951. At least twenty-one dogs were flown in the six years that followed to measure blood pressure, pulse rate, respiration rate and body temperature under conditions of weightlessness and high acceleration. Laika, the dog passenger of Sputnik II, was hooked up with instruments to give the same sort of information. Soviet scientists reported increases above normal in her saliva rate, pulse rate, breathing rate and blood pressure under the high acceleration of the launch period. But these all settled down to normal after she became weightless in orbit.

Apparently, the Soviet Union decided to go ahead with its man-in-space program a short time after launching Sputnik II. It is clear that Russia developed a new rocket especially for manned space flight, which was flight-tested for the first time January 20, 1960. Normally, at least two years elapses between the beginning of work and the first flight test of a large new rocket; indeed, the period may have been longer. Thus the Soviets had been working on their man-in-space program for about a year before the organization of America's Project Mercury. Further, they developed a large new rocket specially for the task; in the United States, the program was built around an existing ICBM.

The new rocket was necessary because Soviet scientists planned to launch a huge craft into space. Instead of the 2500 pounds of weight assigned to the orbiting Mercury capsule, the Red craft was to weigh about 10,000 pounds. The three Sputniks built the Soviet orbital launch capacity up to about 3000 pounds. Their next three space shots, the Luniks in 1959, weighed about 800 pounds apiece. A rocket that lifts 800 pounds to a lunar trajectory is able to put about 5000 pounds in orbit. Thus the Lunik rocket brought them halfway to their goal.

Donald J. Ritchie, a specialist in Soviet rocketry, believes the Lunik first stage was a pair of R-14s plus a pair of 88,000-pound-thrust solid-propellant engines that gave a total takeoff thrust of about 660,000 pounds. This could obviously have been boosted to about 700,000 pounds by substituting the more powerful R-14A for the R-14.

Some readers may ask why the Soviets would go back to a less powerful rocket, the R-14, after the R-14A had proved itself in launching Sputniks II and III. If this is what they did, I believe the reason was reliability. They had plenty of experience with the R-14, which had been flown many times in tests of the T-3 ICBM. The R-14A, although it had proved itself too, was not quite such a standard item of hardware and they probably did not feel the same degree of confidence in it. And so, when they wanted to shoot the moon in a hurry, they fell back on the R-14.

But I think it is likely that they used their most powerful rocket unit for the man-in-space launcher. What else do we know about the rocket? In a statement to the International Aeronautical Federation, the Soviet Union said it had six motors with aggregate horsepower of 20 million. A good guess would be four in the first stage and two in the second. Although there are several ways to convert horsepower into thrust, engineers consider the most likely method to be on the basis of "jet velocity"—the speed of the gas stream. Such a conversion would give a total thrust of 1,250,000 pounds in the two stages. A reasonable breakdown between the stages might be 1,050,000 to 1,100,000 pounds thrust in the first stage and 150,000 to 200,000 pounds in the second stage. Note that four R-14A engines would give first-stage thrust of 1,060,000 pounds. However, some American officials believe the thrust is less than a million pounds.

Between January 20, 1960, and March 25, 1961, Russia launched the new rocket nine times successfully in preparation for manned space flight. There probably were some failures too. The New York Times on February 10, 1960, quoted an unnamed U.S. official as saying that two unsuccessful launching attempts took place in addition to the two successes in January. The story did not make clear whether rockets were launched unsuccessfully or countdowns were merely suspended. The nine launchings included four rocket tests and five orbital flights or spacecraft, four of which carried dogs.

Two failures marred the attempts to return the spacecraft from orbit. The first, launched May 15, 1960, was oriented in the wrong direction when the retro rockets were fired to bring it down four days later. As a result, they had the effect of lifting the orbit higher instead. The trouble was corrected and, when the second orbital spacecraft was flown August 20, it was recovered the next day, with its two dogs, Strelka (Little Arrow) and Belka (Squirrel) in addition to a rabbit, rats, mice, fleas, plants, algae, fungi and seeds.

But trouble developed on the third flight, in which the Soviet scientists evidently attempted to follow the plan intended for the first manned flight. The orbit was lower (apogee 155 miles; perigee 112 miles) than those of the previous two, which reached as high as 228 miles and had perigees about 190 miles. It isn't clear just when the return was attempted, but it may have been done at the end of the first orbit. Soviet scientists were quoted as saying it would have to be done very promptly to prevent the craft from burning up in its natural fall through the denser parts of the atmosphere. In any case, the attempt failed and the dog passengers, Pchelka (Little Bee) and Mushka (Little Fly), and their smaller animal companions joined Laika as casualties of the early exploration of space.

But the fourth and fifth flights, on March 9 and 25, 1961, were successful. Their orbits were quite similar to that of Spacecraft III, but each weighed almost 300 pounds more. Presumably, some heavy piece of equipment was added to straighten out the trouble.

In addition to the orbital flights, Soviet scientists continued to launch ballistic rockets carrying animals. At least four flights of a capsule weighing more than two tons, with one or two dogs and a variety of other animals, to altitudes up to 300 miles, were conducted between the times of Sputnik II and the Gagarin flight.

Meanwhile, Russia was choosing pilots. Soviet spokesmen refuse to say when the selection was made or how many were chosen. As in the United States, however, the candidates were aviators and the best qualified were subjected to careful medical and psychological examination. Then they began a training program. The cosmonauts studied the rudiments of rocket propulsion and space flight, construction of the spacecraft, astronomy, geophysics and space medicine. Their training included aircraft flights in weightless condition, training in a simulated cabin and on a special training machine, long periods in a soundproof chamber, centrifuge tests and parachute jumping. The program seems quite similar to that of the Mercury astronauts in the United States, with the addition of the soundproof chamber. The Russian cosmonauts learned in weightless aircraft flights up to 40 seconds duration that they could eat liquid, semiliquid and solid food normally and that they could perform such tasks as writing, radio communication, reading and visual orientation.

In his flight around the earth, Gagarin reported that he felt perfectly well and that his working ability was not impaired.

He observed the operation of the Vostok's equipment, maintained voice and telegraph communications with surface stations, made observations through the portholes and with an optical instrument and recorded his observations in a notebook and on a tape recorder.

As is well known by now, the sky appears black from space, but the earth has a blue halo. For the blue of the sky is the color of the air. From above, the air appears to change gradually from soft blue through a series of stages until it fades into the black of space. Gagarin also reported that when he came out of the earth's shadow toward the end of his flight, he saw a bright orange glow at the horizon that blended into all the colors of the rainbow.

What do we know about the design of the Soviet spacecraft? Russia has disclosed only the total weight, 10,419 pounds for Gagarin's flight. It is in two major segments, the pilot's cabin and a section for scientific instruments and the retro rockets. However, the two sections can be separated. It isn't clear, however, whether the pilot's cabin is intended to be returned from orbit separately. The two did separate on the first flight May 15-19, 1960. However, the separation could have been part of the malfunction that prevented returning it. On that flight, Russia announced a weight breakdown of 5512 pounds for the cabin, including a dummy man, and 3250 pounds for the instrument compartment. The remaining weight, presumably, was the retro rocket.

On the second flight, August 19-20, 1960, the entire spacecraft re-entered properly but a capsule containing the dogs and some of the rats separated from the main body at an altitude of about five miles and the two landed separately. It now seems evident that this separation was a test of the pilot's ejection seat, a safety measure designed to save his life in case anything goes wrong with the very large parachutes used to bring the spacecraft down. The ejection capsule landed at a speed between nineteen and twenty-six feet per second, the same as in a fall from five to ten feet. The main body of the ship landed with a speed of about thirty-three feet per second, the same as in a fall from about seventeen feet. If the ejection capsule had not separated, the main body would have been heavier and thus would have landed even harder. It seems likely that Russian scientists prescribed a larger main parachute for the next flight. In an announcement

August 24, the Soviet government said that, although a man could have survived the trip, further studies would be made before launching a man.

The Vostok's cabin has three portholes and two quick-opening escape hatches. An air-conditioning system maintains air pressure at the same level as at the earth's surface, with normal oxygen concentration of about 20 per cent, temperature ranging between 59° and 72° Fahrenheit and relative humidity between 30 and 70 per cent. The air is kept fresh by chemical action and circulating liquids in the cabin structure maintain the temperature.

The entire first flight was controlled automatically, by means of instructions programmed on electronic tape after the Vostok had left the range of surface stations. However, the pilot could have taken over the operation of some of the controls had he wished. As the time approached for firing the retro rocket, an electric eye compared the direction of the sun with the orientation of the spacecraft. Any necessary correction must have been provided by small gas jets on the outside surface. Then the retro was fired.

In the event of retro rocket failure, a Soviet statement said, the construction of the craft allowed the cosmonaut to land on earth with the use of the natural braking force of the atmosphere. This would take a long time, however, and so supplies of food, water, electric power and air-purifying chemicals were carried for up to ten days. The entire surface of the spacecraft is covered with insulating material, and other unspecified measures were taken in building the craft to prevent the internal temperature from rising too high during the long period of heating that would take place during gradual braking in the atmosphere.

Several discrepancies appeared in the Soviet account of Gagarin's flight. As a result, some commentators expressed doubt about the story. However, the highest American officials are convinced that the Soviet Union did orbit a man on April 12, 1961. U.S. intelligence agencies have obtained enough information to assure themselves that the major outlines of the story are true. But there are discrepancies as to details. For instance:

The London *Daily Worker,* two days before the actual flight, published a story that an astronaut had orbited the earth three times the previous Friday, April 7, and had landed with serious injuries. Soviet authorities denied the report and U.S. officials said they had traced no satellite launchings from the Soviet Union on that day. Apparently, the story was leaked as a publicity buildup.

One Soviet scientist, Nikolai Gurovsky, claimed that Gagarin parachuted out of the capsule, landed on his feet and walked up to a group of people standing in a field. However, the official account said he remained in the spacecraft.

In Florence, Italy, Anatoly Blagonravov, an academician and a lieutenant general of artillery, was asked at a space conference how Gagarin saw the view from the Vostok. Blagonravov said there were no windows, just a radio indicator. Later, however, the official account declared there were portholes of heat-resistant glass.

Soviet spokesmen have never straightened out a series of contradictions about Gagarin's flight in the neighborhood of South America. The first reports said he radioed a report from over South America fifteen minutes after takeoff. Later the official version changed the timing of the message to 9:52 A.M., Moscow time, forty-five minutes after takeoff. At a press conference on April 16, Gagarin was asked whether South America is beautiful from space. He replied: "Very beautiful."

Actually, Gagarin did not pass closer than 700 miles south of the tip of Cape Horn, and did not reach that point until 10:05, Moscow time, according to the orbital data the Soviet government released. Furthermore, even if he had come within viewing distance of the continent, he could not have seen it because it was the middle of the night. The Vostok did not pass into daylight until it was halfway across the South Atlantic.

Some high U.S. officials believe the Soviet Union encouraged conflicting stories so as to create an atmosphere of doubt and thus keep the world guessing as to the technical details. For, although there have been some changes since the death of Stalin, the Soviet Union is still a closed society, in which secrecy is a way of life. The Soviet authorities want to gain maximum publicity for their cosmonaut's exploit, but they also want to do so with the disclosure of a minimum amount of information.

7. SOME COMPARISONS

LIVE TELEVISION AND RADIO EQUIPMENT, and almost five hundred correspondents, including sixty-one from the foreign press, were present at Cape Canaveral on May 5, 1961, when a Redstone rocket boosted a Mercury capsule to an altitude of 116 miles for the first U.S. manned space flight. The government had invited the world to watch every stage of the proceedings. Correspondents saw Alan B. Shepard Jr. leave his quarters before dawn, drive to the launch site, enter an elevator to ascend sixty feet to the capsule and blast off into space. At the other end of the line, reporters on the aircraft carrier U.S.S. *Lake Champlain* saw him step from a helicopter after he was hoisted from the capsule floating in the Atlantic Ocean 303 miles from Cape Canaveral. There was no doubt in anyone's mind that Shepard did make the trip, modest though it may have been in comparison with the orbital flight of Yuri Gagarin.

Furthermore, an observer was present from the Federation Aeronautique Internationale (FAI), the international aeronautical association that certifies all world flight records. Three months previously, at a meeting in Paris, FAI had approved five new categories of records—three involving flight in orbit and two of suborbital flight. In the discussions, the U.S. member, the National Aeronautic Association, had proposed a regulation requiring the presence of representatives of neutral nations and the FAI at the launching for certification of any flight as a record. The Soviet delegation would not agree to the requirement,

[93

although it left open the possibility it might drop its opposition later.

The National Aeronautic Association arranged for Jacques Allez of France, president of the international body, to watch the Mercury launching. Allez was at the pad when Shepard entered the elevator to the top of the gantry. He was briefed at the blockhouse and then went to the flight control center to observe the takeoff and follow the capsule's progress on a radar plotting board. Later, Allez wrote in a letter to Jacqueline Cochran, president of the U.S. association: "Your government's approval of my witnessing this flight is indicative of your determination to share your scientific progress with the world."

The United States also shared with the world a tremendous volume of technical information about how the flight was carried out. The information included such details as the thrust, size and weight of the Redstone rocket and the modifications made to convert it for carrying a manned capsule; the capsule design and the metals of construction, the viewing ports, the electronic instruments, the tape recorders, the cameras, the gas-jet attitude control systems, the radio communication, the medical sensors, the parachutes, and the rockets carried on board for separation from the Redstone emergency escape, jettison of the escape rockets and re-entry. A month later, at a special scientific conference, doctors made public all of the medical data and Shepard reported on how he was able to perform.

The open nature of the Shepard flight—as well as that of Virgil I. Grissom two months later—generated an extremely favorable reaction abroad. To some foreign observers, the advantage of American openness almost equaled the Soviet technical superiority in being able to launch man into orbit. Neutral observers could not help but contrast the complete, detailed information about every phase of Project Mercury with vague Russian statements such as, "the landing system is switched on at a definite altitude," "the pilot's cabin of the satellite spaceship is much more spacious than that of a plane," and "the air is regenerated with the help of highly active chemical compounds."

However, Russia has begun to relax the secrecy a little—apparently in an effort to court world opinion. To satisfy an FAI requirement to disclose the point of launching, Russia gave the position to the nearest degree of longitude and latitude—65° East Longitude and 47° North Latitude. This located the spot

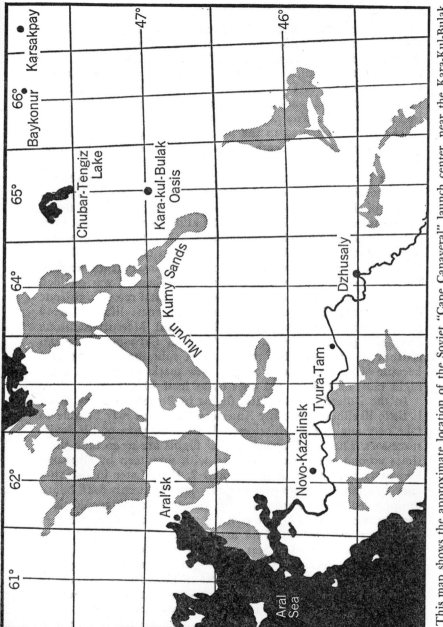

This map shows the approximate location of the Soviet "Cape Canaveral" launch center, near the Kara-Kul-Bulak oasis. Soviet statements have given the longitude as 65° East and the latitude as 47° North. Location was given to the nearest degree; thus it is somewhere within the four boxes centered at Kara-Kul-Bulak.

within a rectangle about 70 miles long in the north-south direction and 45 miles wide. The point of landing, however, was given to the nearest minute—45° 59′ East Longitude and 51° 16′ North Latitude, which reduced the possible area to less than a square mile. The FAI asked for the same degree of accuracy for the position of the launching pad and the Soviet members promised to obtain it. The Soviet members also told the FAI that Allez would be invited to the landing area for future manned flights. There was no mention of observing the launching, however. The map on page 95 will locate the launching area.

Since the Soviet members had not agreed on any requirement of international observers, the FAI certified Gagarin as the first holder of the three records for orbital flight: duration of flight, 108 minutes; altitude, 203 miles (327 kilometers), and total mass lifted, 10,419 pounds (4725 kilograms). It is interesting to speculate, however, on whether the U.S. members of FAI would have agreed to the certification had not U.S. intelligence verified that Russia did orbit a man on that day. Shepard was certified at the same time as holder of the two suborbital records: altitude of 116 miles (186.3 kilometers) and total mass lifted of 4040 pounds (1832.6 kilograms). In the second Mercury-Redstone manned flight on July 21, 1961, Virgil I. Grissom reached an altitude of 118 miles but that was not submitted for a record because of an FAI regulation that new marks in manned space flight must exceed the old ones by at least 10 per cent.

In the United States orbital flights in Project Mercury, there is little likelihood that any American astronaut may be able to take over any of the orbital records from Gagarin or his Soviet successors. The first Mercury orbital flights are to go only three times around the world, compared with seventeen by Gherman Stepanovich Titov on August 6 and 7, 1961. Later in the Mercury program, eighteen-orbit flights, lasting twenty-four hours, are planned. Soviet astronauts will almost certainly exceed these performances first. There was no chance that Project Mercury could take over the record for mass lifted; the Atlas is too small to do the job. Indeed, it was necessary to reduce the weight of the capsule used for the suborbital flights before beginning orbital flights. Grissom's capsule was lost in the Atlantic because of a malfunction in a new escape hatch used to reduce the weight by fifty pounds. The same reason was almost certain to prevent Project Mercury from taking over the altitude record. Altitude requires propulsion power that was not available. Even if the Atlas should manage to boost a Mercury capsule a few miles higher than Gagarin's 203, it seemed certain that subsequent Russian flights, with plenty of boost power to spare, would have outdone him by a wide margin.

Thus it seems likely that Russia will hold the orbital flight records—symbolic of supremacy in space—for some years to come. Why, then, does America go on with Project Mercury? Hugh L. Dryden, deputy administrator of the U.S. space agency, puts it this way: "Are we going to stop the airplane business because somebody abroad flies an airplane? We are going to be in the space exploration business for a long time." Project Mercury is a necessary step in learning to fly men in space. It is a program of learning what men can do under conditions of weightlessness —first five minutes with the Redstones, then one, two and three orbits, and later with eighteen orbits or more. It is a program of learning man's physical and mental reactions to progressively longer flights. It is a program of learning how to build and test spacecraft—developing components and techniques to be applied to larger and more complex spacecraft. Finally, it is a program to develop methods of operating in space. In Project Mercury, the United States is laying a groundwork designed to make it possible to take over the world records from the Soviets later in the decade, when larger American rockets will be available.

In the first two Mercury flights, Astronauts Shepard and Grissom did accomplish one thing that was not done with the Vostoks until the second Soviet flight, by Titov. Both Americans controlled the spacecraft attitude manually. Gagarin left the control to the automatic programmer. The difference between the two is actually not very great because both the U.S. Mercury spacecraft and the Soviet Vostok have alternate capabilities: they can be controlled automatically by the programmer or the pilot can take over manually. To some extent, the difference may have been in the engineers' assessments of the most serious problems to be solved. On the first orbital flight, the Soviet engineers probably were concerned most about checking the operation of the automatic controls on a long flight with a complex system. The American engineers were less concerned about the performance of the Mercury spacecraft on a relatively short flight; thus they utilized the periods of weightlessness to obtain maximum information on how the man performed.

Gagarin, although he was simply a passenger, observed the flight instruments and could have taken over control at any time. Shepard and Grissom controlled the spacecraft attitude but could have returned the operation to the automatic programmer at any time. It should be noted that attitude control is critical in space flight only when rocket power is being applied. The flight of an airplane or glider is controlled, of course, by changing its orientation, and the pressure of the air on its wings and control surfaces forces it to move in the direction desired. But there is no air in space and thus the space vehicle continues moving in a given direction unchanged except for the action of gravity or rocket power. Since the rocket is usually fixed solidly to the spacecraft, it is necessary to maneuver the craft to fire the rocket in the proper direction.

Firing the retro rocket is a critical maneuver for returning from orbit. The speed of the spacecraft must be reduced by about 300 miles per hour from the orbital speed of about 18,000 miles per hour so that it will gradually fall into the atmosphere. If the rocket is not fired in the proper direction, the orbit may be raised higher or simply turned a little. Furthermore, the retro rocket thrust is not aligned perfectly along the center of gravity and tends to twist the craft out of line. Thus, it is necessary to maintain the orientation very carefully while the rocket is firing. Titov attempted control only during orbital flight. He left it to the programmer to bring him back. Data released after Shepard's flight showed that he controlled his orientation well within the allowable error while the retro rockets fired. It was just an exercise on the suborbital flight, of course. The spacecraft would have returned through the atmosphere in any case, because it did not have enough speed to put it into orbit.

The results of the flight gave the U.S. engineers evidence that adding a man to the system increases the reliability of the system. One small example was particularly convincing. After the retro rockets fire on the Mercury spacecraft, the spent rockets must be jettisoned, because they are strapped to the heat shield, which protects the craft from the high temperatures generated when it is entering the atmosphere. A light is to show on the instrument panel after the jettison takes place. On Shepard's flight, the light failed to operate. Shepard, however, heard a bump as the explosive bolts separated, and he saw the straps falling away. Thus he knew the function had taken place. To

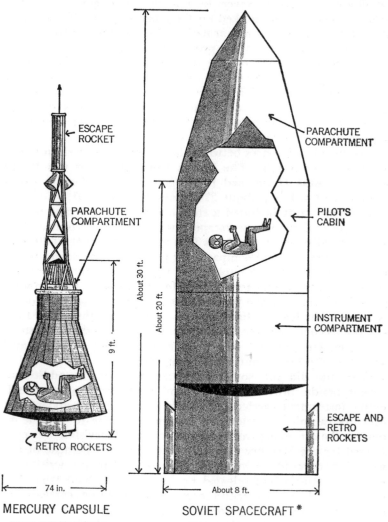

ESCAPE
ROCKET

PARACHUTE
COMPARTMENT

About 30 ft.

About 20 ft.

9 ft.

RETRO ROCKETS

|← 74 in. →|

PARACHUTE
COMPARTMENT

PILOT'S
CABIN

INSTRUMENT
COMPARTMENT

ESCAPE AND
RETRO
ROCKETS

|← About 8 ft. →|

MERCURY CAPSULE

Weight, 3900 lbs. including
escape tower, **2700 lbs.**
without tower

SOVIET SPACECRAFT *

Weight 10,400 lbs.

* Drawn on the basis of photographs
and statements released by the Soviet
government. The pilot's cabin also
includes an ejection seat.

be doubly certain, however, he was able to operate a manual override switch that checked on the retro jettison. The override gave him the desired confirmation. In an unmanned system, there would have been no provision for using human senses. The human operators on the surface would not have been as certain of what happened, and the mechanical equipment might have slavishly followed a program that would have spoiled the success of the experiment. Perhaps similar incidents occurred on Gagarin's and Titov's flights, but Russia has not seen fit to release such information.

The major differences between the Soviet and American spacecraft is in the weight. The Vostok I orbital weight was 10,419 pounds; Vostok II weighed 10,430 pounds. The Mercury spacecraft weight will be about 2700 pounds. The 4040 pounds of the Shepard craft included a steel tower and the escape rocket. In the orbital flight, the escape tower is to be jettisoned after the first halfstage of the Atlas falls away. The great additional weight makes a second compartment possible in the Soviet spacecraft. Also, the pilot's compartment is apparently more spacious than the cramped quarters of the Mercury capsule. From photographs published by the Soviet Union, it appears that the Vostok is about eight feet in diameter and about thirty-three feet long —a twenty-foot cylinder leading into a cone perhaps thirteen feet long. On page 99 is a diagram comparing the sizes and weights of the Vostok and the Mercury capsule.

What use did the Soviet engineers make of the additional weight, besides providing more room? We know of only one scientific instrument carried by Vostok I that was not aboard the Mercury capsules. A television transmitter made it possible to observe the astronaut from ground stations. Television was considered for the Mercury capsule but was rejected because of the weight that would be involved. However, up to the writing of this book, Russia had released no information about what Gagarin carried in his second compartment; Titov carried life specimens. The pilot's compartment, although more spacious, was apparently less heavily instrumented than the Mercury capsule.

The air supply in the Russian craft is maintained at sea-level pressure of 14.7 pounds per square inch, with the normal composition of about 20 per cent oxygen and the rest mostly nitrogen. The Mercury spacecraft, to save weight, uses pure oxygen at a pressure of 5.5 pounds per square inch. A special oxygen bottle had to be designed because those used aboard conventional aircraft were much too heavy. U.S. engineers believe the Vostok uses aircraft air supply systems.

The Soviet spacecraft has supplies of food, water and chemicals for regenerating oxygen to support a cosmonaut up to ten days. The Mercury spacecraft is designed to operate in space only four and a half hours, the period of three orbits. Its oxygen supply is good for twenty-four hours to provide for emergency —in case the capsule should have to float in the water for several hours awaiting the arrival of ships and helicopters. Later in the program, beginning late in 1962 or 1963, a greater oxygen supply will be provided, so as to allow for flights as long as a day. Weight will be found for the additional oxygen supply by eliminating some of the experimental instruments carried on early flights. Longer flights also require more fuel for the gas jets that control the orientation in space. Presumably, the Soviet craft has a much larger supply than the Mercury capsule. The jet fuel capacity is also increased in the later-model Mercury capsule. However, it will be nowhere near the amount the Vostok must need for a ten-day flight.

The Vostok used a different radio frequency than the U.S. Mercury capsule. The Vostok transmitted on a frequency in the 20-megacycle world-wide amateur band, which carries signals around the curvature of the earth, but which is subject to distortion and interruption by the sun's activity (sometimes called sunspots). Russia uses 20 megacycles because its only ground stations are within the borders of the Soviet Union. On major launches, Russia also spots a few ships at strategic points. The United States uses different frequencies. A network of sixteen stations around the world makes it possible for the U.S. astronaut to be in contact with the surface most of the time. The Mercury craft is passed along the chain like a pail of water in a fire-fighting bucket brigade.

On the Soviet spacecraft, all the on-board rockets are at the rear, while the Mercury capsule carries its escape rocket on a tower above. The Mercury jettisons its escape rocket halfway through the firing of the Atlas, so as to reduce the weight that must be put into orbit. The Soviet launching rocket has power to spare and need not go through such a complex maneuver. It may well be that the Russian craft's escape rocket is carried into orbit and does double duty to provide retro propulsion to slow the craft down for re-entry. The Soviet craft also has an ejection seat used for escape under some circumstances. Titov said he landed by parachute in the ejection seat.

All of the differences between the Soviet and American spacecraft do not add up to a factor of three or four, despite that advantage in weight. The Soviet craft is probably capable of supporting two men—indeed, such a flight may take place before this book appears. Titov told a press conference it was possible "in principle" to carry two men in Vostok II, but that the craft was designed for only one. The American designers, under pressure of necessity, have apparently been able to pack much more useful equipment into an equivalent amount of weight and space allowance. "The Russians have built most of their satellites and equipment they have used in a rather rugged fashion," says Abe Silverstein, former director of space flight programs for the U.S. space agency. U.S. engineers believe the Russian craft weighs a good deal more than necessary.

Thus it seems safe to speculate that, if the United States can ever catch up with Russia in rocket boost power, skill at miniaturizing equipment will enable it to do more than Russia. But America is far behind. In February, 1961, Russia added 4000 pounds to the orbital boost capacity of its big rocket, apparently with a bigger second stage. In two successive attempts to send an unmanned craft to Venus, Russia orbited payloads weighing 14,000 pounds. The first failed to launch the Venus craft and, even though the second did send the probe on its way, the radio failed a week later. Nevertheless, the two shots stand as evidence that Russia is steadily maintaining her advantage in rocket size.

8. SATURN

ONE DAY IN NOVEMBER, 1957—a short time after Wernher von Braun's German-American group had won permission to launch a U.S. satellite—von Braun and several of his staff were discussing the project while they sat in a plane speeding across Arizona for a conference in Los Angeles. One of those sitting with him was Heinz Hermann Koelle, a comparative newcomer who had come to the United States in 1955. Koelle, who was now in charge of future planning for the group, part of the Army Ballistic Missile Agency, chose that moment to press a scheme he had worked out to build a large new rocket quickly.

Koelle's idea, which he had advanced as long ago as 1951, was that it would be easier to build a large rocket with a cluster of many smaller engines than by building one big engine. He urged von Braun and a senior adviser, Ernst Stuhlinger, that the time was ripe to begin making proposals to develop a booster rocket with thrust of more than a million pounds. With 20-20 hindsight, we now can see that a similar plan was beginning to be set in motion in the Soviet Union.

However, von Braun recognized the political realities in the United States and told his young planner that the proposal was premature. "Let's forget about it this time," he said. "We want to get a satellite into orbit."

But Koelle did not forget about it. While most of the Army team at Huntsville, Alabama, was toiling night and day to prepare the Redstone and its upper stages for launching America's first satellites, the future projects planner and his staff prepared engineering designs for a four-cylinder booster rocket that would generate thrust of almost one and a half million pounds, compared with 300,000 or 360,000 for the still unflown Titan and Atlas intercontinental ballistic missiles.

After the successful launching of Explorer I, von Braun endorsed the Koelle plan and took on the task of selling it to higher authority, something that would have been impossible a few months earlier because, under the Defense Department's ground rules, no large hardware development job could begin unless there were a specific military application. No one could predict with certainty what use might be made of the capacity to lift large payloads into orbit. Those that could be foreseen did not seem to be sufficiently important to justify the expected cost. Fortunately, however, as a first reaction to Sputnik, the Defense Department created a special agency with the charter to conduct a national space exploration program for a period of one year. The new Advanced Research Projects Agency (ARPA) was to assign jobs to the individual services according to their capabilities, without limitation to those for which a specific military requirement could be advanced.

But there was no complete agreement on whether such a job should be undertaken. Everyone agreed that it was necessary to begin work on developing a new single engine with upwards of a million pounds of thrust. That job would take about five years. "I don't think you can do very much to shorten it," said Herbert F. York, then chief scientist of ARPA. By putting smaller, available engines together, York said, the development time could be reduced to about three years. "It is not as good a way to do it, but if there were an emergency reason for having a million pounds of thrust, one could do it now."

The discussion of whether there was such an emergency occupied six months. And the plan had to be modified to save money. Koelle had proposed a four-cylinder rocket based on an engine of 300,000 pounds thrust that had been partially developed in a low-priority research project. But finishing development of the 300,000-pound-thrust engine would cost $50 million. To save that money, Richard B. Canright and David Young of the ARPA staff conceived a plan to use eight engines of an existing type that required a relatively modest amount of work to make them ready. The existing engine, with thrust of 150,000 pounds, was already in use in the Jupiter, Thor and Atlas missiles. The improvement would increase its thrust to 188,000 pounds, so that the total thrust of the eight-cylinder unit would be one and a half million pounds. ARPA approved the limited program in August, 1958, and committed $15 million to start the work. It was first given the name of Juno V and later renamed Project Saturn.

When NASA began operation in October, 1958, Administrator Glennan asked President Eisenhower to transfer to it the Vanguard group in the Naval Research Laboratory and two Army agencies. The latter were the Jet Propulsion Laboratory at California Institute of Technology and about half of von Braun's Development Operations Division of the Army missile agency. The Vanguard group and the California laboratory were transferred with little argument, but the Army argued that it needed the von Braun group's services to finish work in progress on Army missiles. Von Braun had told a Congressional committee early that year that his group was expending 20 per cent of its efforts on space projects and the remainder on missiles. The Army argument prevailed in 1958.

But in the year that followed, the emphasis of the work at Huntsville shifted. The last Jupiter missile frame was produced there in July, 1959, and the huge fabrication hangar was converted to build the Saturn. The only work remaining to be done on the Redstone and Jupiter missiles was that of converting them for use as space launchers. The only purely military project left was Pershing, a medium-range solid-propellant missile.

Glennan had wanted the von Braun group in the space agency so that its rocket-developing know-how would be available to monitor more intelligently the millions of dollars' worth of work it planned to contract to industry. Also, Glennan wanted to press rapidly with development of the Saturn, which he considered an essential member of a family of space launching rockets of varying sizes.

By the summer of 1959, a scuffle had developed within the military services about Saturn and the von Braun group. Although the Defense Department research agency was committed to the idea of continuing work on long-range projects for which no military requirement could be foreseen, it was difficult to carry out in practice when costs were high and budget money was tight. Large hardware projects like rockets usually do not cost very much in their first year because it takes time to get organized, choose contractors, hire personnel and in some cases construct facilities. The bill rises sharply in the second year and sometimes again in the third. The Defense Department had begun several major programs in the year after Sputnik. In 1959, when the costs began to mount sharply, the squeeze was on. If the department were to stay within the spending limits established by the Eisenhower administration, something would have to go. Saturn, a very expensive project for which there was no specific military requirement, was a natural candidate.

Another factor complicated the picture. The Defense Department decided in September, 1959, that the Air Force would be the single manager of all military space activity. A few individual projects were specified as exceptions. Nevertheless, the directive ruled out at least in principle any idea that the Army would retain the von Braun group. At this stage, the Air Force proposed that it take over the group and the Saturn project. Herbert York, who had now become Defense Department director of research and engineering, asked in a circular to all services which of them had a requirement of a rocket as powerful as Saturn. The Army, charged with developing a military communication satellite, was the only service to reply positively. But then the analysis by the Defense Department showed that even the communication satellite needs could be filled with a somewhat smaller rocket, the Centaur.

At this point, York concluded that there was no military requirement for the Saturn and signed an order canceling it as a military project—thus leaving the door open for transfer of the von Braun team to the civilian space agency. Glennan picked up the signal and renewed his request to the President. York came under criticism when, a few days after he signed the order, a Russian rocket launched an 858-pound sphere carrying the Soviet coat of arms, which became the first man-made object to strike the moon. He was thus portrayed as having canceled the biggest American project to lift very heavy payloads into space. During the furor that followed, York's order was canceled and the Air Force renewed its bid. But the National Aeronautics and Space Council approved the transfer late in October, subject to a Congressional veto. There was no substantial opposition in Congress and the transfer of 4500 Army employees, including 100 former Germans who had worked on the

V-2 at Peenemuende, took place July 1, 1960, at the beginning of the new fiscal year. But many months were lost because of the shortage of funds during the period of controversy, particularly because there was no authorization to pay more than a little overtime. Work on the Saturn did not pick up a full head of steam until early 1960, by which time Russia had already flight-tested its million-pound-thrust rocket.

For von Braun, who must certainly rank among the most single-minded men in recorded history, the establishment of his space rocket center marked the climax of an incredible career in high position of two governments on opposite sides of World War II. He first became interested in exploring space as a thirteen-year-old East Prussian schoolboy. With fanatical devotion, he pursued the idea for thirty-five years, building weapons most of the time, awaiting the opportunity to use his rockets for space travel.

He first encountered the idea of building rockets in 1925, when he saw an advertisement in an astronomy journal for Hermann Oberth's book, *The Rocket to Interplanetary Space*. He bought the book and was dismayed to learn on opening it that it was filled with mathematical formulas. In desperation, the youth asked his teacher how he could understand what Oberth had written. "Study mathematics and physics," the teacher replied.

And so he did. The two subjects were his worst; he had failed both the year before. But he threw himself into them and gradually improved his grades. By the time he was sixteen, young von Braun was the leader in both subjects in his class in the school on Spiekeroog Island in the North Sea. He was graduated a year ahead of time.

As an eighteen-year-old student at the Charlottenburg Institute of Technology in Berlin, he met Oberth, the author of the book, and became a volunteer assistant until Oberth returned to Rumania in 1930. Together with other members of the German Rocket Society (VfR), von Braun took part in the establishment of a launching station—which they called the Raketenflugplatz (rocket airport)—at the Berlin suburb of Reinickendorf. The following year, while taking a summer course at Zurich, Switzerland, von Braun became friendly with an American medical student, Constantine Generales. The two promptly contrived a space-medical research project in which a bicycle wheel, a hand crank and half a beer can were put together to test the effect of high acceleration on mice. Then Generales dissected the animals. They learned that most of the deaths were caused by brain hemorrhage. However, the research was cut short abruptly at the demand of von Braun's landlady, who had found a tell-tale ring of mouse bloodstains on the wallpaper.

Back at Berlin, the rocket group was constantly running out of money for its experiments at the Raketenflugplatz. Rudolf Nebel, the senior member, interested the ordnance department of the German army and the group arranged a demonstration for the army in July, 1932, a short time after von Braun had been graduated from the technical institute as an aeronautical engineer. The rocket rose 200 feet and then veered off horizontally and was pronounced a failure. But army officers told von Braun later they would support the society's work if the members would agree to work in secret at an army installation.

Von Braun, recognizing that steadily increasing sums of money would be needed for metal work, instruments, valves and other forms of hardware, attempted to persuade his colleagues that the only reasonable source was the government—in this case, the army. But the others were reluctant to give up their showplace in the Berlin suburb. And so, on November 1, 1932, von Braun alone went to work as the first employee of the rocket section. The others continued at the Raketenflugplatz for about a year.

Meanwhile, he had enrolled as a graduate student of physics at the University of Berlin. With the facilities available to him at the army installation at Kummersdorf, sixty miles south of Berlin, he was able to perform the experiments for a thesis on the burning process that takes place within a liquid-fueled rocket engine. His design for the injector—a circular metal plate with many small holes like the nozzle of a bathroom shower—is a standard pattern still used with minor variations in modern liquid-rocket engines. The injector provides for the proper mixing of fuel and liquid oxygen in the combustion chamber. He won his Ph.D. two years later but the thesis remained an unpublished secret document until after World War II. With army support, he built up a research staff that built and tested progressively larger rockets.

Interservice rivalry—between the German army and air force —helped von Braun establish the huge test center at Peenemuende. The Luftwaffe offered in 1935 to appropriate five million marks to build the facility. The army, not to be outdone, put up six million. The group moved to Peenemuende in the spring of 1937. As the size of the staff grew, von Braun brought in some of his former colleagues from the Raketenflugplatz. At Peenemuende, the research was aimed at testing techniques to be applied to a weapon that would carry a warhead weighing a metric ton (2200 pounds) to a target 160 miles away—twice the range of the Big Bertha gun of World War I fame.

But von Braun still was gazing with one eye into space. Adolf Hitler visited the Kummersdorf army base March 23, 1939, and von Braun traveled from Peenemuende to give the Fuehrer a briefing on rockets. Colonel Walter Dornberger, von Braun's military superior, warned him not to bring up the subject of space flight. Dornberger feared that Hitler would cut off their funds if he suspected the rocketeers were aiming at anything so impractical. And so von Braun restricted the briefing to the potential of rockets as weapons and auxiliary propulsion for aircraft. At lunch, however, Hitler brought up the subject, saying that he had met Max Valier, one of the early rocketeers, some years previously in Munich. The Fuehrer dismissed Valier as a dreamer. Von Braun was about to defend Valier when Dornberger gave him a sharp glance and made a diplomatic comment that space flight was a long way off. Hitler closed the conversation with a polite comment about the rocket demonstrations he had just seen.

The second time von Braun met Hitler, in June, 1943, the Fuehrer made an essential technical contribution to the development of the V-2. After seeing a film on the V-2, then approaching readiness, Hitler decided to give the highest national priority to producing it. He asked von Braun what the effect of the impact of 2200 pounds of TNT would be. Von Braun replied that there was no practical evidence yet, but as the rocket hit at a speed of 3300 feet per second the shattering force could be expected to multiply the destructive effect of the warhead. Hitler objected, maintaining that a very sensitive fuse would be needed so that the warhead would explode at the exact moment of impact. Otherwise, he argued, the warhead would bury itself in the ground before exploding and the blast would just throw up dirt. Von Braun listened and, when he got back to Peenemuende, ordered an analysis of the Hitler theory. It turned out to be right and the engineers had to develop a new fusing system, without which the V-2 would not have worked.

Hitler had ordered a crash program for developing the V-2 in the fall of 1942, at the midpoint of the war. Afterward, Heinrich Himmler's Nazi organization began to put pressure on the top officials at Peenemuende to join the party. Similar suggestions were made by high party officials with whom von Braun dealt in Berlin. He eventually joined in early 1944 because he felt that further refusal would have been construed as opposition. But his interest in space flight caused him to run afoul of the Nazis. Von Braun tells this story: At a cocktail party in 1944, he remarked to a woman doctor that he had space travel in mind when he developed the V-2 and that he regretted its imminent military use. Meanwhile, Himmler was plotting to take Peenemuende away from the army and to put it under the control of his party organization, the SS. Summoned to a conference in East Prussia in early 1944, von Braun turned down Himmler's proposal. After he returned to Peenemuende, Gestapo agents arrested him early one morning and jailed him for two weeks. A court of SS officers charged him, among other things, with the casual statements he had made to the woman doctor who had informed on him to the Gestapo. But while the trial was in progress, Dornberger arrived with an order for von Braun's release, having told Hitler's headquarters that, if he were kept in jail, there would be no V-2.

At the end of the war, von Braun and the Peenemuende top staff fled westward ahead of the advancing Red Army and eventually surrendered to American forces. A group of 120 was brought to the United States and settled at Fort Bliss, near El Paso, Texas, from 1945 to 1950. Their presence was not welcomed by all Americans. The Federation of American Scientists protested to President Truman that it was "an affront to the people of all countries who so recently fought beside us." But the Germans gradually began to be accepted and, in 1949, they attained the status of immigrants by walking across a bridge to Mexico and then returning. They became U.S. citizens in 1955.

When he came to the United States, von Braun felt freer about advocating space exploration, for he was working for the Army, which recognized its public relations value in obtaining funds from Congress. As missile development progressed in the period after the Korean War, the Fort Bliss group was assigned the job of developing a medium-range ballistic missile for the Army. The missile became known as the Redstone. Later, rivalry among the services developed. No one could produce a formula that would satisfactorily answer the question as to which kinds of missiles belonged to which services. In the intermediate range of 1500 miles, the von Braun team developed the Jupiter for the Army, while the Air Force Ballistic Missile Division developed a weapon with the same engine and almost identical capability called the Thor. However, both weapons were assigned to the Air Force for actual deployment—the Thor in Britain and the Jupiter in Italy and Turkey.

Von Braun's assignment as head of the team demanded more attention to public relations. In Germany, a dictatorial government required only that the Peenemuende organization be on good terms with its army superiors and a few high officials in Berlin. In the United States, it was necessary to sway public opinion. He constantly lectured and wrote magazine articles on space exploration. In 1949, he wrote a book, *The Mars Project,* which circulated among publishers for almost four years before the University of Illinois Press brought it out. He provided consulting services for the Walt Disney motion picture, *Man in Space,* which was released in 1954. Eventually, von Braun came to be regarded in the United States as a symbol of space exploration.

Meanwhile, more of the technical direction was turned over to others on von Braun's staff. His senior deputy, Eberhard F. M. Rees, took over much of the responsibility. Rees, a native of Wuerttemberg, is a mechanical engineer and a 1934 graduate of the Dresden Institute of Technology. He was assistant to the manager of a Leipzig steel plant until a short time before World War II broke out, when he decided to go on an expedition to the mountains of eastern Turkey. On his return, a professor at Dresden recommended that Rees join the Peenemuende staff, which he did in early 1940. At first, he had charge of the machine-tool shop. He became von Braun's second in command about a year later, and has held this position ever since.

There are more engineers than scientists on von Braun's senior staff, although many of those involved in developing the electronic gear have advanced degrees in mathematics and physics. The present membership of the team is considerably different from the 120 who came to the United States in 1945. About a third of this number has dribbled out around the United States, many of them to work for aircraft companies involved in missile and space vehicle development. A small but steady stream has come from Germany to replace them.

But it must be remembered that the vast majority of the staff of the NASA Marshall Space Flight Center is American-born; there are only 100 Germans among a total that will approach 7000 by 1963.

Under the civilian space agency, the von Braun team's first major assignment was to develop Saturn. The Marshall Center is building experimental models of the first stage, the eight-cylinder rocket with one and a half million pounds of thrust, "in house" at Huntsville. After the experimental work is completed, the stage will be produced at New Orleans. The first version of Saturn will have two stages. The second stage, being designed and built by the Douglas Aircraft Company at Santa Monica, California, will generate a thrust of 90,000 pounds. The two-stage rocket will be able to lift into orbit a satellite weighing about ten tons.

Flight tests of the first stage began in late 1961, but the second stage, which uses a radical new fuel, was not to be flown until 1963. The new fuel is liquid hydrogen, which must be kept at a temperature of 423° below zero Fahrenheit, just 36° above absolute zero. Although technical problems had to be solved, the civilian space agency decided in early 1960 to switch to liquid hydrogen because its performance is about 30 per cent higher than kerosene on a pound-for-pound basis. Also, the NASA engineers believe that the United States is ahead of Russia in liquid hydrogen technology and should press the advantage.

Saturn will be the second U.S. rocket to have an upper stage that burns liquid hydrogen. The first will be the Centaur, which will use such a stage atop an Atlas ICBM. The Centaur, which was to begin flight tests early in 1962, will have a carrying capacity close to that of the rocket that launched the first Soviet manned spacecraft. Saturn will be the first American rocket to exceed it.

In this chapter, I have discussed only the first model of Saturn, the C-1. Several larger versions are proposed and will be discussed later. Data on all major U.S. rockets are in the Appendices.

9. APOLLO

ONE DAY SOON—possibly early 1964—three Americans will climb into a spacecraft 150 feet above the ground, halfway up an arch-shaped tower on Complex 34 at the northern end of Cape Canaveral. A few hours later, a two-stage Saturn will rise from the pad and carry them into orbit about the earth.

The astronauts will be riding in a spacecraft called Apollo. They will lie on padded couches as the Saturn first stage takes them off with thrust of one and a half million pounds, subjecting them to an artificial gravity that steadily rises over a period of 144 seconds from one and a third to six and a quarter times normal gravity. Then the eight-cylinder first stage falls away and the second stage takes over with a much more bearable 90,000 pounds of thrust. They may be able to move about during almost eight minutes of second-stage burning, while the artificial gravity rises from seven-tenths of normal to about three times normal.

On the Apollo flight, the primary control will be on board, in the hands of the three-man crew. This will mark a change from Project Mercury, in which the Mercury Control Center at Cape Canaveral is in charge. The crew will fly the Apollo more like an airplane, once the countdown is over and the vehicle is off the ground. The control center, like the control tower at an airport, will give clearance for takeoff, provide radar and other position information, and route traffic. But the spacecraft crew will be basically on its own.

The crew will even be able to exercise some control over the firing of the Saturn, although its guidance system is operated primarily by an electronic computer. Most course corrections will have to be made more rapidly than a man can react to what he sees on his instrument panel. But the astronauts will be able to monitor the activity and to take some actions if necessary in periods when they are not hampered by excessive gravity, such as during the long burning of the second stage. The automatic guidance and control system of a modern rocket is an improvement of the automatic pilot, which has become standard aircraft equipment. On an aircraft, the human pilot does not attempt to override the automatic pilot except when the machine is malfunctioning. Similarly, the astronaut-pilot on board the Apollo will normally allow the guidance and control system to orient the space vehicle while the Saturn stages are firing and to set the time of cutoff. But he will watch for any obvious breakdown and will be ready to take over the controls to perform whatever maneuver is necessary to get the ship back on course.

Like the Mercury capsule, the Apollo will be equipped with an automatic system that will sense any impending catastrophic failure of the Saturn stages and will fire an escape rocket on a tower above them to get the spacecraft away. The escape rocket will be operable by the crew or, in emergency, by the ground control. It will be jettisoned as in the Mercury flights, after the first-stage firing ends.

Once in orbit, the astronauts will be free to take off their space suits and stow them in a locker. The double walls of the Apollo contain adequate protection for their air supply, which is maintained at normal sea-level pressure. They need the suits only to protect them against possible emergency during takeoff and landing. The living compartment, called the command center, has tight but sufficient space for three men. It is shaped like a cone, from thirteen to fifteen feet in diameter at the base and about twelve feet long.

Besides the controls, the capsule will have a food locker, scientific equipment, sanitary facilities and recreational equipment.* Food, water, oxygen and other supplies can be carried for flights lasting from two weeks to two months. But the first flights will probably be shorter.

* Robert R. Gilruth, director of the NASA Space Task Group, is sometimes asked whether there will be women astronauts. He replies with tongue in cheek that 125 pounds is allotted on the Apollo for recreational equipment.

The early orbital flights will be to relatively low altitudes, although the Saturn and the on-board rockets will have the capacity of boosting the Apollo higher. Above 500 miles around the earth's mid-section, the lower radiation belt begins to create a severe hazard to man. On a mission to deep space, it may be possible to pass twice through the belts—once out and once back —but flying repeatedly through them on orbit will be quite dangerous. In later years, when very large booster rockets are available, it may be practicable to build spacecraft with heavy shielding to protect against the radiation. But on the Apollo, the shielding will be limited to that provided by the necessary structure and equipment. The Apollo command center must be held to a weight of four to six tons. Thus weight will be too precious to allow the addition of any heavy metal just for shielding. A second segment, called the service module, will carry scientific instruments, oxygen supplies and other gear.

Attempts at reaching higher altitude will be made in gradual stages on subsequent flights. The problem involved is not merely the rocket power required. The more critical question will be that of return. For, just as rocket thrust must be achieved to reach a high orbit, it must also be applied to reduce the orbit to the level where the natural braking of atmosphere takes effect, just below 100 miles of altitude. This is the major function of the propulsion module, the third segment of the Apollo space-craft.

The astronauts will also use the on-board rockets in learning to maneuver—to change orbits and speeds with the idea of per-fecting techniques of rendezvous in space. The rendezvous tech-nique is expected to provide the most likely ultimate means of assembling large orbital space stations. It also may provide a method of making the trip to the moon with smaller rockets that would otherwise be necessary. Later, I shall discuss the problem of lunar transportation in detail.

The rendezvous technique would provide for the possibility of rescuing the crew of a disabled spacecraft. For instance, if the retro rocket of a spacecraft in orbit should fail, a rescue vehicle could carry up a powered return capsule or a new retro rocket. Rendezvous would also make it possible to do repairs on disabled unmanned spacecraft. The military services are in-terested in developing the technique so that it will be possible to inspect possibly hostile satellites. The Air Force began work in 1960 on a project to conduct rendezvous experiments with unmanned satellites. Late in 1961, NASA approved a project for developing a two-man spacecraft with the aim of carrying out orbital flights by 1963 and rendezvous experiments by 1964.

When the time comes to return to the earth, the astronauts will don their space suits again and strap themselves into their couches. The only time they might need the suits during the flight in space would be in case of an unexpected emergency requiring some sort of repair job outside the Apollo. In that case, the repairman could make use of an airlock at the tip of the cone. Such a job would be undertaken only in case of desperate need, however, since the space environment is extremely dangerous to an astronaut protected only by a space suit. The greatest hazard is not the vacuum but the sun, whose most harmful radiations are absorbed by the atmosphere and do not reach the surface of the earth. The repairman must be careful not to look toward the sun, lest he be blinded. In the shade, a man in a space suit would have to have heating pads—probably something like electric blankets—to prevent him from freezing as his body radiates its heat away.

On the return trip, special insulating material on the Apollo's surface will prevent it from burning up like a meteor as it plunges into the upper air at a speed of almost 17,000 miles an hour. Unlike the Mercury capsule, which had heat protection only on the blunt end, the Apollo will be protected all over the outer surface. It will also have movable control tabs, like the rudder and ailerons of an airplane, which will make it possible to maneuver the craft after it returns to the atmosphere at much less cost in weight than additional retro rockets would require. The insulating material on the afterbody will protect it from the heat of friction with the onrushing air during control maneuvers. The Mercury capsule, which falls like a rock, has no controls. Its aerodynamic shape keeps the blunt end down. To save weight, insulation is installed only on the part that faces the air stream.

The Apollo will be maneuverable even when the shock of plunging into the atmosphere heats the surface to temperatures in the thousands of degrees. Maneuvering the capsule will be possible because its shape—like that of the Mercury capsule—gives it a moderate amount of what aircraft designers call "lift." In an aircraft flying horizontally, lift is the upward pressure created by the flow of air, which keeps it from falling. But when a craft is plunging downward from space, the action of lift tends to move it horizontally and thus curve its path away from that of a free fall. The degree of maneuverability is determined by the ratio of lift to drag—the latter being the force exerted by friction, backwards for an airplane flying horizontally and upwards for a falling object. The following diagram will show what I mean:

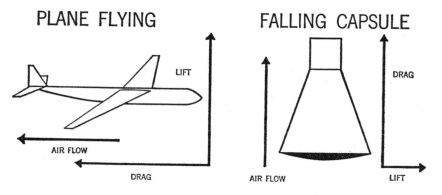

A winged vehicle has a lift-drag ratio of two or more; that is, its lift is at least twice as great as its drag. The Mercury capsule has a lift-drag ratio of 0.4. Even the degree of maneuverability provided by that lower ratio is not used, of course. Apollo will have a lift-drag ratio of 0.5; the lifting force will be half of the dragging force. Such a ratio is much too small to fly the craft to a landing; thus it still must use parachutes. But, by manipulating the control tabs before the parachutes deploy, the astronaut pilot will be able to vary the point of landing by several thousand miles along the line of flight and several hundred miles to the right or left. Normally, of course, the controls will be operated by automatic equipment, but the pilot will take over when he believes it necessary. There may, however, be a few seconds when the crew cannot function, when the artificial gravity caused by the deceleration rises to twelve or more times normal.

Ordinarily, the Apollo will come down on dry land, although it will be able to set down in the sea like the Mercury capsule in an emergency. It will have two parachutes for the last phase of the descent. A small "drogue" parachute will slow it at high altitude and a large main parachute will deploy for the last 10,-000 feet or so. Although the flight path is under control, a fairly wide landing area is still needed to provide for the possibility that the craft will be blown about to some extent by unpredictable winds during the parachute phase. A strong candidate for selection as the landing spot is Edwards Air Force Base, near Muroc, California, a huge dry lake that has been the base of the X-15 and other advanced research aircraft.

Two of the three men in the Apollo crew—the pilot in command and a copilot-navigator-flight engineer—will probably be men whose names are already well known. It seems likely that they will be chosen from the astronauts who have qualified themselves on orbital flights in Project Mercury. Some additional test pilots will be recruited, of course, to provide a sufficiently large pool of candidates for later Apollo flights. But the third crewman will be an entirely different type of man. He will be a scientific observer.

The observer will have to be in the same fine physical condition as the pilot astronauts. And he will be trained in operation of the flight controls and instruments, so he can fill in for the pilot and copilot in case of an emergency. But his major qualification will be his scientific standing. There will probably be no elaborate process of selecting scientific observers, as in the case of pilots. Rather, officials of the space agency expect to receive and evaluate suggestions made by the scientific community. The Space Science Board of the National Academy of Sciences may be asked to make some nominations of promising young scientists who have had experience undergoing conditions of extreme hardship, such as on Antarctic expeditions.

What will the scientist do in orbit? He will operate scientific instruments. He will conduct physiological and psychological experiments to learn how well men adapt to space flight. He will carry out experiments in the life sciences with animals, plants and other living specimens. Finally, he will prepare himself and develop techniques for the flight to the moon.

"Man's first flights into space must be considered in the character of a training venture," says Lloyd V. Berkner, chairman of the Space Science Board of the National Academy of Sciences, "since there is very little that man can do in empty space that instruments cannot do better. After all, instruments can be exposed to all of the elements that we wish to study in space, while man must be shielded from the very things we wish to observe."

But man on the moon or the planets is something else again. First of all, the speed of light limits the possibility of remote control over instruments on distant astronomical bodies from the earth. Light and radio waves travel at a speed of 186,000 miles a second. The moon is 250,000 miles away. If you are operating instruments on the moon by remote control from the earth, it takes a second and a half for a radio signal to travel back to earth and tell you something has happened. After you decide to react, it takes your signal another second and a half to return to actuate your robot explorer. Thus there is a built-in delay of three seconds between event and response, perhaps long enough for the robot to fall off a cliff and smash to bits. On another planet, automatic control is even more difficult. At its nearest passage, Venus is twenty-six million miles away from the earth. The radio signal would take 140 seconds to travel between the planets and almost five minutes for the round trip. The round-trip thirty-five million miles to Mars at its nearest conjunction would take almost seven minutes. When the planets are at other portions of their orbits, the distance can range up to more than 200 million miles and the round-trip signal to more than thirty-five minutes.

In the approach of an interplanetary spacecraft to a planet, Berkner says, "a ten to twenty-minute delay time in control response is a long time, so it will be difficult to manipulate precise controls from the earth. While instruments conceivably could do the job, man will probably be superior in controlling them."

"From a scientific standpoint, there seems little room for dissent that man's participation in the exploration of the moon and planets will be essential," declares the Space Science Board, "if and when it becomes technologically feasible to include him. Man can contribute critical elements of scientific judgment and discrimination in the exploration of those bodies, however complex and sophisticated they may become."

The primary purpose of the Apollo flights in orbit about the earth will be to prepare for those to the moon—first around the moon and then to the lunar landing. In many respects, the spacecraft will be the same for all three flights. The command center will be unchanged. The on-board rockets will vary according to the amount of maneuvers required. But the major difference will be in the size of the launching rocket.

In its first few flights, the Apollo will have a fighting chance to capture some of the Soviet records for orbital flight. Russia's early cosmonauts will probably have flown longer duration flights than will be possible to exceed immediately, but America may be able to take over the records for altitude and mass lifted. The orbital Apollo spacecraft will weigh almost ten tons, about twice the weight of the Vostok. However, Russia probably has larger craft in development. Indeed, because of the Soviet lag in miniaturization, Russia may *have* to build a heavier spacecraft to orbit a three-man crew.

America's best chance to forge ahead with the orbital Apollo flights will be in the altitude class. American scientists already have learned much more than those of Russia about the nature of the radiation belts; still more investigation is planned in the early years of the decade. There are many possible orbits that will reach higher altitudes without entering the intense portion of the radiation belts. Among the logical early missions with Apollo will be the search for such passages between the inner and outer belts—like the quest for the Northwest Passage to India that occupied many of the early explorers of North America. The superior American scientific knowledge of the radiation belts and the maneuverability that will be provided by the Apollo propulsion module may make it possible for American astronauts to be the first to fly at altitudes in the thousands of miles.

All of the Apollo orbital flights, however, will be in preparation for flights to the vicinity of the moon. The astronauts must learn to operate in the space environment and they must test the craft's equipment for the more ambitious flights. But before they fly to the moon's vicinity, the engineers must build, test, fly and make reliable bigger rockets than Saturn. The time required for developing the rockets largely sets the timetable for the lunar flights; the rocket work will take up the better part of the decade.

III

SOME BENEFITS
EN ROUTE

10. PROGRESS IN SCIENCE

TO THE SCIENTIST, rockets and spacecraft are merely new laboratory tools, which enable him to perform experiments that were previously impossible. He judges their utility in terms of the value of the experiments and the knowledge they are likely to produce. In comparison with other kinds of laboratory tools, rockets and spacecraft are very expensive. Sometimes scientists ponder the expense, in comparison with the lower cost of tools for work in other branches of science, and conclude that the money should be spent elsewhere. They find it difficult to justify the great cost of space exploration on purely scientific grounds.

As I indicated in Chapter 1, however, we justify activity in space by summing up a whole series of considerations—science, utility, inspiration, national prestige, military value and the sheer sweep of history. Only a portion of the cost should be charged to science. Nevertheless, there are real and valuable scientific benefits to be obtained.

How do we measure scientific value? This is an almost impossible task. The role of science is to learn facts, to solve mysteries. The scientist is motivated by curiosity. Often he has almost complete disregard for the practical applications of the knowledge he gains. It remains for other men, often many years later, to find uses. We cannot know in advance what knowledge will be gained by exploring the universe. And so we cannot even speculate on its worth.

But there is another measure of the value of knowledge. It is the simple, direct measure of what interests people. We need not take a Gallup poll to establish a universal human interest in the nature of the sun, the moon, the stars and planets, which have always been up there, beckoning but unattainable, a mystery throughout the ages. Now that technology has made them reachable, the people of the world want them explored.

What are the new scientific tools? Beginning in the late 1940s, "sounding" rockets became available for up-and-down flights carrying instruments where they could make observations for short periods above most or all of the earth's atmosphere. Since 1957-58, orbiting satellites have been available to investigate that region for longer periods. In 1959, objects were launched beyond the reach of the earth's gravity, to make the first investigations of other portions of the solar system. And in 1961, man himself climbed into outer space to begin preparations for the day when his senses would supplement the instruments. Until these new tools became available, all knowledge about the cosmos was indirect, based on what could be deduced from the nature of light and other radiation reaching within the atmosphere.

Each new tool opens new opportunities of investigation. The sounding rocket made it possible for the first time to measure directly the properties of the ionosphere, an electrified portion of the atmosphere, that reflects radio waves. Simple and relatively cheap, the sounding rocket continues to be used for experiments with light payloads at relatively low altitudes. Satellites have just become a standard tool. Science is still in the early stages of making use of them for a multitude of purposes. And the investigations of deep space and what men can do have barely begun. To some extent, scientific use of these new tools must lag behind their development by engineers. The first requirement is to get the instruments out where they can do their work. The most imaginative experiment is worthless if the hardware fails to perform properly. And so, in early test flights of new rockets and spacecraft, experiments often can be carried only on a "space available" basis.

It is interesting to observe that, despite Russia's many technical accomplishments in space, most of the scientific results in the first few years came from the U.S. space experiments. I have recounted earlier how Russia's Sputnik II made the first observations of the great radiation belt, only to have America's James

Van Allen make the discovery and receive the credit, and how many scientific advances were made with the use of the grape-fruit-sized Vanguard satellite. There seem to be two reasons why the U.S. space program is more productive. First, the United States has launched many more satellites than Russia—three times as many by late 1961—and has been able to conduct a wider variety of experiments. Second, U.S. officials suspect that Soviet scientists have not been in close contact with the military authorities in charge of rocket launchings, with the result that the program is not closely attuned to scientific achievement. American scientists, however, do not disparage the quality of the work done by their Soviet colleagues. The general levels of proficiency and the numbers of scientists engaged in space research are about equal in the two countries, according to U.S. estimates.

A partial explanation of the difference between the two nations' programs is in the difference between the forms of hardware available. Russia performed its early space investigations with a few variations of one large launching rocket, capable of carrying very large payloads but very expensive. Russia is not as wealthy as the United States and thus the cost of rockets must have influenced the USSR more in deciding how many to launch. Russian scientists made the most of each expensive satellite by packing as many experiments aboard as possible. The American researchers, on the other hand, did not have very large rockets available. But U.S. industry has learned to produce somewhat smaller rockets in volume—some for military needs and some for space exploration. Although hampered by stringent requirements to hold weight down, the Americans were able to follow up questions raised by findings with one satellite by launching a similar but slightly different experiment a short time later. As the United States develops more powerful launching rockets, it plans to launch large multipurpose satellites too. But at the same time, the United States is developing cheaper, small satellite launch rockets so as to maintain flexibility.

Scientists play a major role in the U.S. space administration (NASA). The deputy administrator is Hugh L. Dryden, a distinguished aerodynamicist who performed some of the earliest investigations of airfoils near the speed of sound. The scientific phase of the work was headed for three years by Abe Silverstein, one of the nation's leading authorities on powerplants for high-speed aircraft and missiles. Silverstein's deputy was Homer E.

Newell, upper-air researcher and a leading expert on sounding rockets, who was in charge of the science program of Project Vanguard.* In 1961, the space administration set up an Institute for Space Studies near the campus of Columbia University in New York City, to conduct theoretical research in astronomy and the space sciences, which it hopes will encourage the scientific community to take more interest in space investigation. The director is Robert Jastrow, a brilliant young nuclear physicist who received his bachelor's degree from Columbia in 1944 at the age of eighteen, and who was with Project Vanguard before he took charge of theoretical studies for the space agency in 1958. NASA has many other outstanding scientists on its staff, and receives advice from a special Space Science Board of the National Academy of Sciences headed by Lloyd V. Berkner.

What are the scientific uses of space vehicles? Jastrow and Bruno Rossi of Massachusetts Institute of Technology have broken them down into four major categories.† They are (1) investigating the region traveled by the vehicle; (2) studying the earth by viewing it from above; (3) examining the radiation from the sun, planets and stars that does not pass through the earth's atmosphere; and (4) exploring the moon and planets. So far, most scientific investigation has been in the first two categories.

In the first, of course, was the 1958 discovery of the Van Allen belts, which surprised the scientific world even though almost all of the theory necessary for predicting their existence had been developed beforehand and one physicist, Fred Singer of the University of Maryland, had written a paper speculating on the existence of such a belt of charged particles a year before. Other results in this category include measurements of magnetic fields, atmospheric density, micrometeorites (dust particles) and the properties of the ionosphere.

In the second group, viewing the earth, are weather research, geodetic measurements of our planet's overall dimensions and studies of how the ionosphere transmits some radio waves around the earth's curvature. Weather researchers are particularly interested in the mechanics of transfer of the sun's energy to the

* In a 1961 reorganization, Silverstein took over the Lewis propulsion laboratory in Cleveland, and Newell became head of the scientific programs.
† "Results of Experiments in Space," a chapter in *Science in Space*, edited by Lloyd V. Berkner and Hugh Odishaw, McGraw-Hill, New York, 1961.

earth; how much is absorbed, how much is reflected and how the local weather is affected by variations in the rate of absorption and reflection. I shall go into the weather experiments in some detail in Chapter 13. The geodetic work includes findings about the earth's oblateness and pear shape, such as the Vanguard results. The best results on the ionosphere have been made possible by the Soviet Sputniks, which transmit at two radio frequencies affected in different ways by the ionosphere. U.S. work on sounding the ionosphere from above has been hampered by rocket failures, but a heavy schedule of firings is to begin in 1962.

Many astronomers consider Category 3 the most interesting. For when we look at the sky from the earth's surface, we perceive only a few octaves of the vast keyboard that makes up the electromagnetic spectrum, which extends from the shortest gamma and X-rays to the longest radio waves. The atmosphere transmits radiation through only two "windows." One is the visible light region plus a little in the infrared and ultraviolet areas. The other is a band of radio wavelengths between one centimeter and about forty meters. Everything else is absorbed. By launching rockets above the atmosphere, astronomers can send instruments to a region where they can "see" the remaining kinds of radiation—the short-wave ultraviolet and X-rays at the high end, the infrared and very short-wave radio in the middle of the keyboard and very long-wave radio at the lower extreme. Thus far, only a few rockets and satellites have observed the cosmos in these forbidden wavelengths.

Even less has been done in the final category, exploration of the moon and planets. Two Soviet moon shots, Lunik II and Lunik III, launched September 12 and October 4, 1959, constituted the total of man's lunar exploration up to the writing of this book in 1961. Lunik II, which fell to destruction on the moon, made a negative measurement of the lunar magnetic field —that is, the field if it existed was too weak to be detected by the instrument. Lunik III, which flew around the moon, secured crude, blurred photographs of the side that faces permanently away from the earth. Their most interesting feature is a chain of mountains apparently 1200 miles long, which Russia has named the Soviet Mountain Range. If their existence is confirmed by later and more detailed exploration, lunar specialists will have to revise a currently held theory that mountain-build-

ing forces—erosion and wrinkling of the crust resulting from
slow shrinking—have not been present on the moon. According
to the theory, the mountains on the visible surface appear to be
crater walls and formations of debris left by the impact of large
meteorites.

Space research cuts across established areas of science. It uses
the talents of specialists in physics, astronomy and the earth sciences. Recently, biologists have become interested in the possibilities of learning about forms of life elsewhere. They hope to
acquire information that will shed light on the origin of life on
earth.

An even more fundamental question that may be answered by
exploring space is the origin of the solar system. Astronomers
generally agree that the sun was formed by the gradual collection
of bits of matter together under the force of gravitation. The
theory currently in favor holds that the planets were formed the
same way. It is hard to find evidence one way or the other on
earth, however, because the weather has washed it all away in
the four and a half billion years that have passed since the earth
was formed. The same will probably be true of the planets. But
there is one object in the sky that has not changed much since
the solar system was created. That is the moon, which has no
atmosphere and thus no weather. And unless the Soviet finding
of a mountain range proves to be true, the topography of the
surface itself may be similar to that of billions of years ago.
Study of the interior of the moon can provide a strong indication of whether it was formed by a collection of bits of matter,
for if so, it probably never had a molten interior. If a solid core
of iron is found in the moon, it will be evidence it was formed
in some other way. The first American unmanned spacecraft to
land on the moon—in the Ranger series—will carry seismometers
to record "moonquakes" and obtain information on the moon's
interior.

Many scientists believe the most exciting current area of space
research is the relationship between the sun and the earth. It is
certainly the most active. Almost all scientific satellites, and even
some launched for other purposes—seem to produce new understanding of how the sun's energy provides the motive force for
earth processes. The solar energy output is almost constant,
mostly in the visible and near-visible range of wavelengths that
are transmitted through the earth's atmosphere to the surface. But

there are violent fluctuations in a small part of the production —a part that consists of X-rays, ultraviolet light and charged particles that are almost completely absorbed by the atmosphere. Some of the most profound effects on earth are apparently caused by the charged particles—protons and electrons—which the sun spits out in great clouds from time to time.

The solar eruptions, called flares, can be compared with storms on earth; flare activity is sometimes called solar weather. If a flare is pointed in the right direction, the cloud of particles reaches the earth and interacts with the ionosphere, the Van Allen belts and the earth's magnetic field. The effect on the ionosphere interrupts long-range radio communications by breaking up the electrified layers that reflect short-wave radio waves back to earth. The lower tips of the radiation belts spread hundreds of miles from their normal habitat near the north and south magnetic poles, making their presence visible with brilliant red auroras in the northern and (near the Antarctic) southern skies. Magnetic needles all over the earth begin to jiggle in a "sudden commencement" as the shock wave preceding the cloud encounters the earth's magnetic field. The connection between solar activity and these effects had been suspected for some time, but it was not proven conclusively until 1959, when Luigi G. Jacchia of the Smithsonian Astrophysical Observatory at Harvard University published a series of analyses of satellite orbits—first Sputnik II, and then Vanguard I and Sputnik III.

Jacchia showed that all three satellites were slowed in flight every twenty-seven days, the period of the sun's rotation, as though something came out of one active area of the sun and encountered the earth each time around. And on two occasions, he observed a sudden increase in the drag on Sputnik III about a day after a major solar flare, the same time that a magnetic storm took place on earth. Scientists debated for a while whether the atmospheric drag increased because the sun heated the upper air, causing it to expand, or whether the arrival of the solar particles caused heating.

A measurement the following year provided a third explanation. The greatest solar storm in almost five years began November 12, 1960, at a time when the United States had in orbit Echo I, which was a thousand times more sensitive than previous satellites to the drag of the trace of atmosphere several hundred miles up. Echo, a 100-foot balloon that weighs less than 200 pounds, is extremely sensitive to drag because of its large surface area, in comparison with its weight. For several days after the storm Echo decelerated about twice as rapidly as beforehand, and then the rate fell back to normal. Even for the big balloon, the changes involved were tiny. Its period of revolution about the earth—approximately 117 minutes—increased "normally" at about a second a week. During the solar storm, the weekly rate increased to two seconds.

Dramatic confirmation of the effect of solar activity came from several other satellites. Measurements made with Explorer VI, a satellite launched by the United States August 7, 1959, showed the outer Van Allen belt lost particles in some energy ranges and gained some in others. At the same time, an aurora was observed below. More details come from Explorer VII, launched October 13, 1959. On November 28, the satellite passed through the outer belt at an altitude of 600 miles over Montana, while a ground observer was photographing an aurora. The satellite's Geiger counter recorded a great deal of erratic activity. When it passed that way the following night, most of the particles had left that part of the belt.

In the spring of 1960, man-made celestial objects provided two simultaneous views of a solar event. Pioneer V, launched March 11, followed a deep-space trajectory to explore the region of the solar system between the orbits of the earth and Venus. A cloud of particles from a solar eruption reached Pioneer V and the earth March 31, at a time when the two were separated by about three million miles. On the earth, a typical magnetic storm occurred. On Pioneer V protons and electrons were detected in the cloud at the same time as a decrease in the intensity of very high-energy particles from outside the solar system—the so-called cosmic rays. This cosmic-ray effect, called the Forbush decrease after its discoverer, Scott Forbush of the Carnegie Institution of Washington, previously was believed to occur only near the earth. The theory was that it had something to do with the earth's magnetic field. Explorer VII, orbiting the earth, recorded the same increase in solar protons and the same Forbush decrease in cosmic rays. But the number of electrons it encountered in the outer radiation belt decreased sharply during the first few hours and then increased to about fifty times normal during the next week.

Perhaps I had better stop for a discussion of what is now

known about the Van Allen belts. The existence of two major belts is certain; one or more smaller belts may exist between the major belts. The inner belt, the more concentrated of the two, is shaped like a doughnut and surrounds the equatorial regions, beginning at about 600 miles altitude and extending to perhaps as high as 2000 miles. The outer belt covers a much broader region, dipping down over the magnetic poles and swinging outward so that it begins about 10,000 miles over the equator and stretches out as far as 35,000 miles. The inner belt seems to consist mostly of protons mixed with a mixture of energetic electrons and nuclei of heavier elements. The high-energy particles in the outer belt apparently consist mostly of electrons.

The inner, proton belt is very stable. It seems to change very little under the influence of solar activity. The outer belt, however, is extremely erratic. Why is this so? The proton weighs 1840 times as much as the electron; other constituents in the inner belt are even heavier. These heavy particles have much greater momentum than electrons. When a cloud of protons from the sun encounters the earth's magnetic field, it does not have enough energy and momentum to produce a very marked effect on the inner belt, which is pretty much held in place by the strength of the earth's magnetic field and the high energy of its particles. The solar proton cloud may squash it a little but that will be all. However, the cloud acts like a big broom on the lightweight electrons, sweeping the outer belt relatively clean for a while. No one knows just what happens next, but possibly the self-contained magnetic field of the solar cloud opens "chinks" in the magnetic barriers that ordinarily prevent electrons from entering the outer belt and a large buildup takes place for a while. Then the excess electrons may leak down to the atmosphere by way of the polar regions, creating auroral displays as they do.

The effect of the sun's activity on the earth's magnetic field itself is perhaps the most complex of all. It is certainly one of the hardest for the layman to understand. Before the International Geophysical Year, earth scientists could not agree on the cause of magnetic storms. Some believed the sun to be responsible for the almost simultaneous jiggling of compass needles all over the world that constitutes the sudden commencement of a magnetic storm. Others questioned the theory, maintaining that something within the planet, or perhaps the disturbance of a great

"ring current" circling the earth in space, was responsible. However, worldwide IGY observations during the great storm of
February 10-11, 1958, left little doubt of a connection with a
solar flare that had occurred two days earlier.

But the most telling evidence remained to be produced by
Explorer X, a satellite launched 145,000 miles into space March
25, 1961, with an extremely sensitive magnetometer aboard.
Explorer X was fortunate enough to leave the earth a day before a solar cloud sped toward the earth as the result of a flare.
When the cloud arrived, the satellite was more than 100,000
miles farther from the sun. The usual sudden commencement
took place on earth, twenty-eight hours after the flare, indicating
that the cloud was traveling at a speed of about 54,000 miles a
minute. In two additional minutes, the cloud traveled another
100,000 miles and triggered the magnetometer on the satellite.
It is hard to imagine a more beautiful demonstration.

But the Explorer X experiment raised more questions than it
answered. Its magnetometer jiggled sharply—and then stopped—
five hours *before* the solar flare. And another jiggle took place
six minutes after the flare—far too soon for the arrival of particles unless they were traveling at the speed of light. Can solar
flares be predicted in advance by detecting magnetic jiggles in
deep space? Is the magnetometer a tool in solar weather forecasting? Will solar forecasts make it possible to launch manned
expeditions at times of minimum danger from the sun? James P.
Heppner, an outstanding young specialist in magnetism who was
in charge of Explorer X, smiles and replies that more research
is needed before any such conclusion can be drawn.

But Heppner is convinced that a magnetometer can be of
great value in manned spacecraft. Measurements by Explorer X
and earlier satellites have established that the magnetic field is
extremely stable in the region close to the earth. Thus a magnetometer can provide exact measurements of altitude.

What does the future hold in the way of scientific research in
space? We can only predict what tools will be used. We have no
idea what will be learned. The uncertainty is part of the ex-
citement. In the early years of the decade, the United States will
continue to launch special-purpose satellites to follow leads
developed in early investigations of the radiation belts, the ionosphere, magnetic fields, atmospheric density and other conditions near the earth. Beginning in early 1962, the first scientific

instrument will be landed on the moon. That same year will provide the first American opportunity to investigate Venus, the easiest of the planets to reach from earth. Venus and earth come close together late in the year; an exploratory craft would have to be launched in the month of August or wait until the next opportunity, in 1964. In 1966 or 1967, the United States hopes to land instruments on Venus and Mars to determine whether life exists there. During the early years of the decade, satellites will be launched to keep close watch on the sun from space.

Beginning in 1963 or 1964, the United States plans to take advantage of larger rockets it expects to have available to launch larger, more complex multipurpose scientific spacecraft. The most ambitious is the Orbiting Astronomical Observatory, an automatic spacecraft shaped like an octagonal prism, nine and a half feet long and six and a half feet in diameter, weighing a ton and a half. The observatory will have several telescopes aboard, including one with a reflecting mirror thirty-six inches in diameter, comparable to that of a medium-sized observatory on earth. A spectrometer will separate the radiation from celestial bodies into all the wavelengths, including those that do not reach the earth's surface. Pictures of the sky will be transmitted to the earth by television techniques to verify the direction in which the instruments are pointed. The fine pointing control of the satellite's stabilizing system will be able to track a star with an accuracy of a tenth of a second of arc—which is equivalent to focusing on an object as big as a basketball 500 miles away. The launching rocket will be the Atlas-Agena B.

Another ambitious project is Surveyor, which is to make the first American "soft" landings on the moon at about the same time. Surveyor will carry several television cameras with variable magnification, so as to examine the lunar terrain in detail, with stereo vision. It will send the views back to whichever one of the three sensitive receivers of the U.S. space agency's deep-space network, at California, South Africa and Australia, happens to be facing the moon. Surveyor will have a drill capable of boring up to five feet below the lunar surface, to obtain samples for analysis with spectrometers—which determine chemical composition by measuring the wavelength of light the samples reflect. Other instruments will determine density, magnetic permeability, electrical resistivity, heat conductivity and hardness. The samples will also be studied to determine the presence of organic compounds, which might indicate that primordial life forms have collected in the dust generated over the moon's lifetime of four billion years. In addition, Surveyor will sample and analyze the tenuous lunar atmosphere, record moonquakes, and measure gravitation, radiation and the magnetic field, if any.

The Surveyor will be a package weighing 2500 pounds as it enters the flight toward the moon. Most of the weight, however, will consist of a retro rocket that will be designed to slow it to a landing speed between five and ten miles an hour, so it can land gently on its three legs. The lunar landing package will weigh 750 pounds. An offshoot of Surveyor will be a project to launch a spacecraft into a precise orbit about the poles of the moon, by about 1965.

Surveyor will follow a somewhat simpler lunar landing project, called Ranger, designed to land a crushable package striking the surface at more than 200 miles an hour. The Ranger carries a seismometer and a thermometer protected to survive the impact. Outside the protective package, it has a television camera and a special spectrometer for recording very short wavelength gamma rays, to send signals back to earth up to the moment of impact, when they are destroyed. Ranger weighs 750 pounds, like Surveyor, mostly representing the retro rocket. The moon capsule weighs 300 pounds. It is launched by an Atlas-Agena B rocket. Surveyor will be launched by the more powerful Atlas-Centaur.

For investigating the neighborhood of the earth more intensively, the U.S. space agency is planning to launch in 1963 or 1964 a large multipurpose satellite called the Orbiting Geophysical Observatory. The OGO will weigh 1000 pounds and will have compartments for as many as fifty different experiments. The first such satellite will go into a highly elliptical orbit, which will carry it out 70,000 miles. The second, about a year later, will explore the regions over the poles at much lower altitudes, between 150 and 650 miles. These satellites will have enough power supply and space, so that an experiment can be put aboard at almost the last moment, without necessitating change in the design of the overall satellite. They will be launched on a fairly regular schedule, picking up as passengers whatever experiments happen to be ready at the time; an experiment that misses one will be able to catch the next. The arrangement will introduce a great deal of flexibility to the plans for scientific experiments, which now must be tied to rigid launching schedules.

I have chosen only a few of the scientific spacecraft for purposes of illustration. A more complete listing of projects can be found in the Appendix.

As the spacecraft grow in size with the lifting capacity of U.S. launching rockets, they grow more complex and thus more subject to failure. Each component, no matter how reliable individually, has some likelihood of failure. Adding it to the system increases the chance of system failure at least slightly. As the number of components grows, the chance of failure grows almost inevitably. Thus there is considerable risk that many of the more complex spacecraft will have short lifetimes. The problem may be most serious with those that cost the most to build and launch.

What can be done? This is one point at which man in space becomes valuable to science. If the problem of rendezvous can be solved, there seems to be no reason why the astronaut cannot be a repairman. Many failures in spacecraft will prove to be simple to set right, if only a man can get there to do it. It is logical to speculate that some of the manned rendezvous experiments planned for 1964 and later will include attempts to repair malfunctioning scientific spacecraft.

But the exploration of space is not, as I said, a purely scientific endeavor.

11. GEOPOLITICS

NIKITA KHRUSHCHEV takes a long view of history. In the current East-West struggle, he asserts, victory is inevitable for the system he calls socialism. "The socialist world is expanding; the capitalist world is shrinking," declares the Communist Party of the Soviet Union. "Socialism will inevitably succeed capitalism everywhere. Such is the objective law of social development. Imperialism is powerless to check the irresistible process of emancipation."

The Soviet economy is growing so fast, Khrushchev boasts, that it will exceed the U.S. economy by 1970 and, by 1980, will leave the U.S. economy far behind. Capitalism, he finds, has entered the final period of decay; it may flourish a while in a few countries, but it is on the way out. He predicts that revolutions will take place at different times in different places—first in the regions populated by the colored races and formerly held or dominated by the imperialist Western powers. By implication, he predicts that the West will eventually be surrounded and impotent.

The Soviet leader makes no secret of his plans. He rocognizes that a program of national and worldwide import must be elaborated so that those in the ranks will carry it out. He has enunciated his aims frankly and consistently in speeches and interviews with the press. In recent years, the most detailed program was laid before the Communist Party congress of 1961.

The party program called for two decades of work to increase the Soviet national income fivefold, to provide vastly expanded social welfare benefits and to improve living standards, with the use of science and technology as a tool. By agitation and the example of the success of the Soviet system, the party program says, the uncommitted nations will be won over to the "socialist" camp.

But how can a new state advertise its successes? As long ago as the 1930s, Soviet leaders recognized the propaganda value of grandiose projects, quite apart from their practical use. Some of the Soviet state's first major propaganda successes came from the building of great river dams, railroad lines and even whole cities in the former Siberian wilderness. The process was continued after World War II. But until 1957, the world still thought of Russia as a somewhat backward nation. Thus the world was impressed when she announced the successful testing of an intercontinental ballistic missile. But the real shock came two months later, when the Sputniks began flying in orbit.

For Khrushchev, the Sputniks did double duty. On the one hand, he could declare to neutrals that they were a purely scientific endeavor, a peaceful effort to explore the cosmos. "We solemnly declare," he would say, "that we are making man's continued conquest of nature to serve the welfare and happiness of all mankind." On the other hand, they were a clear demonstration, for all the world to see, that Russia possessed a missile that could be boosted into orbit; traveling 5000 to 6000 miles was simpler. By hitting the moon, the Russian Lunik demonstrated that an ICBM could hit the United States. U.S. scientists could argue with some limited justification that the guidance problem involved in hitting a specific American city was more severe than hitting the moon. But such a sophisticated argument could not be heard in the hubbub; it was pointless in any case. If Russia did not have the guidance at that particular point in time, she obviously soon would.

In earlier times, great powers advertised their military might by conducting impressive army parades, by sending warships to neutral ports, and, more recently, by staging aeronautical displays. In the modern age, testing of nuclear and hydrogen bombs has come to be regarded by neutrals as in poor taste, even when it is done underground and thus produces no fallout. Space shots impress everyone and offend none.

Khrushchev times major international moves by his space shots. In 1959, Soviet rockets hit the moon and then flew around the back just before he visited the United States. In May, 1960, the first test of the Soviet manned spacecraft was conducted just before the Paris summit conference.* He visited the United Nations in the fall of 1960 at a time when Soviet missile-tracking ships were in the Pacific to track a Soviet space shot. But the rocket failed and he had to pound on the table at the UN to attract attention. In August, 1961, after the 17-orbit flight of Gherman Titov, he tightened the screws on Berlin and announced plans to build a hydrogen bomb five times as big as the largest then in existence.

Khrushchev has succeeded in getting the world to accept accomplishments in space as a yardstick to measure progress in the technological competition between the United States and the Soviet Union. "Actually, the feeling is not too far wrong," says General Bernard A. Schriever, commander of the Air Force Systems Command. "Major accomplishments in space do require great depth in technology."

It seems safe to predict that Khrushchev will continue to use his cosmonauts' successes as he has in the past—to advertise Soviet technology to the underdeveloped nations, to shake his fist at the West and to use the occasions for building up national morale. But we must ask another question. Will the Soviet Union in fact make military use of its capacity to fly men in outer space?

Before we attempt to answer this question, let us examine the history of flight. Balloons were used extensively in the U.S. Civil War for reconnaissance. At the beginning of World War I, airplanes were used for the same purpose. It was not until later in the war that planes dropped bombs and fought one another in the air.

Space flight has reached the stage where it is being used for reconnaissance. The U.S. Air Force has two such programs, MIDAS (Missile Defense Alarm System) and SAMOS (Satellite and Missile Observation System). Midas is a satellite with extremely sensitive detectors of infrared (heat) radiation, which is designed to detect missile launchings on the ground below. Samos carries cameras designed to photograph the land below. The film is

---

* Some U.S. observers believe the Soviet shot, which took place May 15, 1960, actually had been scheduled for May 1, the day an American U-2 photographic reconnaissance plane was shot down after flying over the launch site east of the Aral Sea.

then ejected from the satellite in a capsule and returned to the earth.

Both programs were in the experimental phase as this was written, but the Air Force was pressing both with the hope of bringing them to operational status in the early years of the decade. Samos, in particular, enjoys very high priority because of the prospect that it may replace the U-2 plane. The capsule-recovery technique and some of the Samos components were being tested in the Discoverer series of Air Force satellites.

But, unlike the airplane, there seems to be no practical reason for using satellites as bombers. Compared with the relatively simple problem of launching missiles from one point to another on earth, putting a bomb in orbit and then returning it is a far more difficult affair. It isn't impossible, but it would require a much larger rocket and far more complicated guidance equipment. Furthermore, there doesn't seem to be much advantage. It is true that a missile base on earth makes a fixed target on which enemy missiles can be trained. But a satellite is a "fixed" target too. Its orbit can be calculated very precisely and methods can be developed to neutralize it almost as soon as it can be put into operation. Certainly, a bomb in orbit has no more effective military value than a ballistic missile on a movable platform, such as a submarine, a plane, a surface ship or a railroad car.

The disadvantage of a bomb in orbit is a fundamental physical fact based on the difference in the speeds between any satellite and the earth below. It is an obviously wasteful process to speed an object to 17,000 miles an hour just for the purpose of slowing it down again to land on an earth target. Any really practical military use of satellites should take advantage of the difference in velocity.

It is still very early in the game, but some scientists believe the satellite may have potential application as a platform for anti-missile missiles. They reason that a missile traveling the intercontinental distance reaches a speed of 15,500 miles an hour, only about 2000 miles an hour less than that of a satellite. Thus if a satellite happened to be in the area, it might be able to intercept the missile with a relatively small change in speed, using a relatively small rocket. A system of such satellites, orbiting over the area where enemy missiles would reach maximum altitude on flights toward the United States, conceivably could provide a workable missile defense. The U.S. Department of Defense is studying such a system in a project called Bambi, which was in a very early phase when this book was written. There was no expectation that such a system could be brought into operation before the last years of the decade, if then.

Bambi is in competition with a much more thoroughly developed anti-missile system called Nike-Zeus, which is an improvement in the Nike series of anti-aircraft missiles. The Nike-Zeus is a ground-based missile that uses a very high thrust solid-propellant rocket, extremely powerful, long-range radar and electronic computers. Batteries of Nike-Zeus weapons would be stationed near all major targets in the United States. When the radar detected a missile on the way, it would feed the data on its trajectory into the computer. If the computer found that the missile was heading for the target area protected by the battery, it would automatically fire the first two stages of the three-stage rocket, calculating and programming its guidance so as to intercept the incoming missile. A second radar, more accurate but with shorter range, would follow the Nike-Zeus interceptor to verify that it is following the right path. If not, it would fire the third stage to correct the path as needed.

The Army, which is in charge of developing Nike-Zeus, says most of the technical problems have been solved, and has asked several times for permission to begin production of the missile, so that Nike-Zeus batteries can be installed to protect American cities from nuclear attack at the earliest possible date, perhaps before the middle of the decade. But scientists of the Department of Defense are dubious about how effective Nike-Zeus can be against missiles falling at speeds of more than 15,000 miles an hour. The department has deferred the decision on the multi-billion-dollar production and installation program until the weapon's effectiveness is demonstrated. Beginning in 1962, the Army expected to hold tests of Nike-Zeus anti-missiles fired from Kwajalein in the Marshall Islands against Atlas missiles launched from Vandenberg Air Force Base in California.

Satellites can perform several functions of practical value for both military and civil applications. In later chapters, I shall discuss communications and weather satellites, the two most important. Precise navigation at sea is a third. The U.S. Navy is establishing a system of satellites called Project Transit, which will send radio signals enabling submarines and ships to plot their positions to an accuracy of a tenth of a mile. The accuracy is required by the submarines that carry the Polaris missiles, so that the gunnery officers can program the missiles accurately to hit enemy targets. But the Navy plans to publish frequencies and other necessary technical information, so that all ships may use it, regardless of nationality.

Another civil-military application of satellites is mapping the distances between the continents more accurately than they are now known. The information makes possible more accurate aiming of intercontinental ballistic missiles. It is also of value to geologists studying the earth's physical composition and over-all dimensions. Several U.S. geodetic satellites are planned.

The U.S. Air Force is grappling with the question of defense against possibly hostile military satellites. The first technical problem to be solved is that of inspecting foreign spacecraft. For several years, the United States has had powerful radar, sensitive optical equipment and other electronic devices stationed at strategic points to learn what they can about Soviet missile and space launchings, and to track Soviet satellites. Obviously, however, closer investigation may make it possible to learn more. Under a project called SAINT (Satellite Inspection Technique), the Air Force is working to develop a method of near-rendevous, so that it might bring an American satellite close enough to a foreign craft to inspect it in space. But rendezvous is a tricky business.

There is a growing belief among spacecraft engineers and scientists that man can be of great value in rendezvous maneuvers. Like an automatic pilot, a machine can be programmed to carry out the necessary maneuvers, but its equipment must be extremely complex. Supervision by a skilled pilot could probably prevent many equipment malfunctions. Furthermore, even the most sophisticated machine can deal only with situations it is programmed to handle; it is incapable of dealing with the unexpected. The machine may concentrate more effectively on a problem, but man is more adaptable. And for the task of inspection itself, once near-rendezvous is achieved, the man is far superior. He can diagnose a situation and recognize patterns or objects—tasks that are very difficult for any machine.

We know so little now about what man can do in space that it is too early to specify in detail what military tasks he can carry out. However, James E. Webb, U.S. space administrator declares: "I think it would be a very brave man who would say that the capacity to operate with large manned vehicles in space would have no military value." First, we must develop the capacity. The military applications, if any, will become clear later. Why must we do so? President Kennedy comments: "We cannot possibly permit any country whose intentions toward us may be hostile to dominate space."

The initial manned space flight program is assigned to the civilian space agency, and under the direction of civilian scientists and engineers. Later on, when basic information is available on what manned vehicles can and cannot do, the military services may follow with spacecraft designed to accomplish specific operational tasks. Interim steps may take place, however, between the stages of pure research and military operation. The military services may wish to carry out research aimed at developing capabilities of importance for operational space flight.

For example, the Mercury capsule is making the first U.S. investigations of what one man in a space vehicle can accomplish in a low orbit for periods up to four and a half hours. But the Mercury capsule-recovery method would be a logistic nightmare in any attempt at operational use by the military services. A small fleet is necessary to recover the Mercury capsule at sea. Its maneuverability is zero after its retro rockets have fired. Military men insist they must have a simpler method of landing at a chosen spot on land, and that the craft have the capacity of maneuvering in the atmosphere.

The obvious method of providing such maneuverability and operational simplicity is to add wings, so that the pilot can glide to a landing field. There are two disadvantages. First, any winged craft must weigh at least 30 per cent more than it would if shaped like a Mercury capsule; the percentage may, in fact, be higher. Second, development of a winged spacecraft takes more time, because the engineering problems are more difficult. In a race to put men in space early, a winged vehicle must be ruled out completely. Furthermore, there is obvious scientific advantage in carrying a larger crew in future flights and so it is logical that the shape is maintained in the two-man rendezvous spacecraft and the Apollo.

But it is equally logical that the military services, which may require winged vehicles if they are to make operational use of space, should take steps to develop the capability. The Air Force, in cooperation with the civilian space agency, is doing so in the Dyna-Soar (Dynamic Soaring) Program. At present, the Dyna-Soar development is in an experimental phase, working toward flight of a manned vehicle in orbit by 1964 or so. The first phase of the program will be designed to develop the techniques of launching and recovering the winged craft. In another phase, later in the decade, Dyna-Soar may develop into a weapon system, whose exact nature will depend on the information gained earlier, both in the Dyna-Soar program itself and in the Mercury and Apollo man-in-space research.

Misunderstanding of the differences between the military and civilian programs has caused some controversy between the Air Force and the National Aeronautics and Space Administration. Some people have professed to see duplication and overlapping between the two man-in-space programs. But there need be none if each stays within its own bailiwick. The job of the civilian space agency is to explore the unknown, to extend the frontiers of knowledge, to be a scout for the advancing army of technology. Once its explorers have learned to fly in one zone and have obtained the basic scientific information on the hazards and man's capability there, they should strike out for another frontier, with lunar landing as the goal. The Air Force, in fulfilling its function of conducting whatever military operations are to be conducted in space, should wait until the scientific information is available before moving to develop operational vehicles. Of course, the military services themselves may wish to fill gaps in the basic research programs of scientific agencies.

Thus the operational military exploitation of any zone of space will inevitably be a few years behind the first scientific explorations. In Project Mercury, suborbital flight takes place in 1961, orbital flight by 1962. The Dyna-Soar orbital flights will take place in 1964 or later. While the Air Force is developing operational techniques for one-man flights into orbit, the explorers are flying crews of three in orbit in the Apollo. The total experience will make it possible to decide rationally whether a manned station in low orbit has any military value. "We must be well advanced in this technology," says Senator Robert S. Kerr, chairman of the Senate Space Committee, "to avoid its possible exploitation against us."

It is difficult to visualize the form the military exploitation might take, because we know so little at present. Vice Admiral

John T. Hayward, Deputy Chief of Naval Operations (development), believes that a manned orbiting space station might provide a base for intercepting ballistic missiles in flight. Others have speculated that manned stations might hold strategic positions in space, such as the "Northwest Passages" between the radiation belts. Other, more outlandish, speculations have been lifted from the Buck Rogers cartoons.

One can make a strong case now against any suggested military use. But none of the most highly placed scientists in the U.S. government feels wise enough to state with certainty that there will be none in the years to come. Prudence, then, dictates that the nation explore space vigorously.

The moon itself has very little foreseeable use in affecting a war on earth. Establishing a missile base on the moon would be fantastically expensive in comparison with the cost of launching a missile from one point to another on earth. It is true that the missile would be falling toward the earth at a greater speed and therefore harder to intercept. But the engineering problems and cost apparently prohibit any such project for many years to come.

Some military men visualize the moon as "high ground," possession of which might make it possible to dominate the approaches. On the last portion of a voyage to the moon, a spacecraft is moving very slowly as a result of deceleration by the earth's gravity. Presumably, it would be an easy target for missiles launched from the moon's surface. There are two obvious arguments against this theory. First, it has not been proved that there is anything of sufficient military value on the moon to make worthwhile the tremendous effort required to establish missile bases. But more important, in the early years of lunar exploration, men will be so exhausted from their battle with the environment that they will have no energy left to fight one another.

The Antarctic provides a good example of how hostile environment draws men together. Scientists and explorers of the United States, the Soviet Union and a dozen other nations occupy that continent on the most friendly terms, sometimes visiting one another's installations for weeks and months at a time. An international treaty reserves the continent for peaceful purposes. The U.S. government often has proposed that outer space be reserved, like Antarctica, for peaceful purposes. In 1959, the

United Nations General Assembly voted to hold a conference on the peaceful uses of outer space in 1960 or 1961. But agreement could not be reached on details of the conference.

So long as the Soviet Union holds primacy in the capacity to fly men and large space vehicles, it may be unrealistic to expect that any agreement can be reached. Furthermore, the United Nations may not be the proper forum for discussions. Only two nations are space powers at present and the space club is not likely to have any new members for a decade or so. A bilateral agreement between the United States and the USSR may be a more practical approach. But to sit at a conference table on equal terms with the Soviet Union, the United States must build up its space capability. Fortunately, technology has not yet reached the stage at which space weapons can be built. There still is time for diplomatic action to head off an arms race there.

"The manned lunar landing," says General Bernard A. Schriever, "creates a specific national objective around which the nation conducts a program to achieve the capacity to travel in space—for both civilian and military purposes. The program demands logical, extensive, large-scale improvement of the United States' technological ability. All the mechanics of operation involved in a lunar landing and return—propulsion, guidance, rendezvous, controlled landing—are vital to the U.S. military posture."

In October, 1960, Schriever related, he appointed a committee of industrialists and scientists to advise on what activities the Air Force should undertake to improve the U.S. posture in space. Trevor Gardner, former Assistant Air Force Secretary, was chairman. "The committee looked at the total picture, both military and civilian, because the two are inseparable," Schriever said. "These things became apparent:

"First, we need the capability to put large payloads into orbit, even though crystal-clear military requirements are hard to establish right now. Many applications will become clear, once we establish the capability. Second, we need the capability of rendezvous, for the transfer of fuel supplies. Third, we need the capability of re-entry from orbit to maneuver and land on earth."

He maintained that orbital re-entry must be established in all three major regimes—with a ballistic shape like the Mercury

capsule, with a lifting body like Apollo and with winged vehicles like Dyna-Soar.

I asked General Schriever, a stern, youthful-appearing officer
who has had charge of the Air Force missile and space programs
since 1954, whether he was unhappy that the lunar landing assignment had not been given the Air Force. "No," he replied,
"the important thing is that the job is done. I have only one
concern. The military must be a full participant in this venture
so that our resources can be most effectively used, and so that
the program can provide the maximum payoff in the form of
national security." But he added that "there is no question that
the top people in this administration are thinking along the
lines of an effort to provide just these things."

He predicted that the Air Force and the civilian agency will
work well together, once the lunar landing effort is organized.
"Any time you set up a new agency," Schriever remarked, "there
will be growing pains in establishing the interface. But I have
more difficulty in establishing the interfaces within my own
command. There will be problems, but I predict they will be
solved."

12. COMMUNICATION
BY SATELLITE

OR THE METRIC MILE RUN at the 1964 Olympic Games in Japan, Wilbur Johnson, a young executive in a Chicago mail-order concern, had what amounted to a pavilion box. From where Johnson and his wife, Emily, sat they commanded as good a view as that provided the Olympic judges. And they were decidedly more comfortable than the judges, whose faces glistened with perspiration in the summer heat.

The Johnsons leaned back in their chairs and sipped cooling drinks while the race progressed. But they edged forward as an American and a Russian matched stride for stride in a final furious dash at the finish. While the huge crowd roared, they saw the two runners almost as if at arm's length. They could all but hear the snap of the tape as the winner broke it. They could almost smell the blossoms that a group of Japanese girls showered on him. . . . Almost, but not quite.

For the hypothetical Johnsons and millions of others throughout the world watched the 1964 Olympics at home on television. A global communication system using satellites made possible live transmissions around the curvature of the earth, despite the difficult fact that television signals travel only in straight lines. TV signals are not reflected from the ionosphere like some forms of radio waves.

The Olympic signals were flashed from a Tokyo transmitter to a satellite orbiting from north to south over the mid-Pacific.

The satellite carried a transmitter that rebroadcast the signals to special sensitive receivers hooked up to national networks in both North and South America. Although it was mid-morning in Japan, the Johnsons watched the event, broadcast live, just before bedtime in Chicago. Another satellite, moving northward over the Indian Ocean, picked up the Tokyo telecast and relayed it to a few stations in Australia, Asia and Africa. A third satellite, heading south from the Arctic over western Siberia, transmitted it to Europe. The event was broadcast live from stations in Australia and Eastern Asia. But in Europe and Africa, where most people were asleep, the stations recorded it on video tape and saved it for morning newscasts.

The above paragraphs are not fantasy. The feasibility of communication satellites has been demonstrated in a series of experiments and the U.S. and other governments are working with private industry to develop a usable satellite system as soon as practicable. The odds are better than even that by 1964 a system will be in partial operation, enough to provide limited live coverage of a few events outside the United States. It will doubtless also be available to transmit around the world the great debates in the United Nations, the inauguration of the U.S. President on January 20, 1965, and the launching of men into space from Cape Canaveral. And it will bring into the Johnsons' home events of comparable importance abroad.

Progress in U.S. communication satellite technology has been so rapid that David Sarnoff, chairman of the board of Radio Corporation of America, said in mid-1961, "We are very close to the achievement of global television as well as other forms of worldwide communications." With this, James C. Hagerty, news chief of the American Broadcasting Company, agrees and says that if present research is pressed he has no doubt that direct live coverage of the 1964 Olympics will be practical. Lloyd V. Berkner, chairman of the Space Science Board of the National Academy of Sciences, declares, "In principle, satellites can multiply the quantity of long-distance communications by a factor of perhaps 10,000."

Although it will certainly be the most spectacular use of communication satellites, ocean-spanning TV will be very expensive and thus available only to report events of transcendent worldwide interest. On the level of daily concerns, however, a satellite system will provide a solution to a problem that vexes the communication industry—how to provide facilities for an explosive growth in demands for overseas transmission of voice, telegraph and electronic messages. Indeed, if it were not for satellites, it is hard to see how the required facilities could be created.

The number of overseas telephone messages from the United States alone has been growing about 15 per cent every year, so that the total doubles every five years or so. Between 1959 and 1960, the growth was 20 per cent. As new nations emerge in Africa and Asia, and as economic development continues in other parts of the world, the rate may increase further. As a nation's economy rises, its requirements for communication climb in almost direct proportion to its per capita income. Businesses, governments and the people themselves want more telephone and telegraph service, not only within their own countries but with the rest of the world. The world total of telephones, which stood at 300 million as the decade began, is expected to reach a half billion by 1980.

And while the number of phones increases, the proportion of overseas calls is growing too. In 1945, only seven overseas calls were made by every 1000 phones in the world—despite the tremendous demands of the armed forces in the final year of World War II. When the war ended, the rate continued to climb, until it reached 25 per 1000 phones by the end of the 1950s. The American Telephone and Telegraph Corporation, which handles all of America's overseas telephone business, believes that as many as 200 overseas calls may be made from each 1000 telephones by 1980. If the rate and the world total of phones grow as predicted, 1980 will bring annual demands for 100 million overseas calls, compared with 7 million a year at the beginning of this decade. These telephone requirements, plus an expected comparable increase in needs for private lines for business and government, could occupy as many as 12,000 message circuits. In the current state of cable technology, this number of circuits would require about 50 telephone cables under the sea.

Short-wave radio, reflected by the ionosphere, is also used for long-range telephone communications, but it is unreliable because it is subject to interruption by solar flares. Also, only a few radio frequencies can be used. And they are being used to capacity. In the higher microwave frequencies, which are not quite as crowded as the other parts of the radio spectrum, the signal travels in a perfectly straight line, like a ray of light, and thus cannot be transmitted reliably more than about 30 miles between two points because of the curvature of the earth's surface. On land, long chains of microwave relay stations 30 miles apart have been built to provide long-distance telephone and television transmissions. But such a system would of course be impractical for crossing oceans.

It is, of course, possible to provide for some of the needed service by laying new submarine cables. In the early 1960s, new cables are to be opened between the U.S. mainland and Europe and Jamaica, between Puerto Rico and Antigua, and between Hawaii and Japan. But laying cables is a terribly expensive proposition. AT&T, which is in business to make profits, has looked into the costs and has concluded that a much cheaper way to do it would be to use satellites instead of tall antenna towers, so that straight-line microwave transmissions from a single satellite will cover a wide area of the earth's surface. The keys to the cost situation are the life and reliability of satellites and the level of demand. Hugh L. Dryden, deputy administrator of the civilian space agency, has compared the economic problems of a communication satellite network with those of an airline. It costs a great deal of money to fly airplanes on schedule or to launch satellites on schedule. But if the seats in the airplane are mostly filled, and if the communication channels of the satellites are mostly used, they can be very profitable, if they last long enough to be amortized.

There are, of course, technical problems that must be solved before satellites can be brought into operation. A great deal of research and many experimental launchings must precede the establishment of an operational network. But the technical problems seem to be straightforward. Almost all of the scientists and engineers familiar with them predict they will be solved in a relatively short time.

But there are nontechnical questions that could delay progress. First, who is to own and run the system? Second, what about assignment of radio frequencies?

Before we look into the question of ownership, let us see how things are done at present. In many countries of the world, telephone and telegraph services are run by the government as a national monopoly. In the United States, private enterprise performs the function under government regulations. The American Telephone & Telegraph Corporation provides all overseas telephone service for American customers, by agreement with whatever foreign agency, government or private, handles service in a given foreign country. Several other companies operate radio and cable telegraph communication services overseas, but AT&T operates more than 80 per cent of America's international electronic communications.

When experiments demonstrated in 1960 that communication by satellite is feasible, AT&T decided to pour a great deal of company money into applied research with the aim of solving the remaining technical problems. To carry out experiments in space, the big utility asked the U.S. space administrator, T. Keith Glennan, to make rockets and launching services available for company experiments. AT&T said it would pay the cost.

A proposal that a wealthy private corporation pay part of the cost of the space program had an obvious appeal to the economy-minded Eisenhower administration. However, Glennan was concerned that AT&T might "pre-empt" the government research program, leading technical development along lines most favorable to that company. And so he advised the company that the government would conduct research from an impartial point of view regardless of what was done by private industry. But he saw an advantage to the government in having the private work done as well. The space administrator anticipated that delays might occur when the research work was completed, waiting for the time when private enterprise could begin work on the commercial system.

The United States had an advantage evident in satellite communications, Glennan believed, which should be capitalized upon in the competition with the Soviet Union for world prestige. If delay should occur in the organization phase, the advantage might be dissipated. As a result, Glennan advised AT&T that he favored making the rockets available, and declared his position publicly October 12, 1960, in a speech at Portland, Oregon.

For operation and ownership of the communication satellite venture, there are three obvious alternatives. One is government; a second is a private company, such as AT&T; the third is a joint venture, with multiple owners including private companies and possibly foreign governments.

Whatever the virtues of government ownership, there are practical political objections. Establishing a government-owned

agency to enter the telephone and telegraph business in competition with existing private industry would certainly require
an act of Congress. Getting such legislation through Congress
would entail a titanic struggle, possibly taking several years.
Furthermore, there are practical reasons why such a step, creating duplicating services, would not be in the public interest.

On the other side, there are equally great political objections
to turning over a lucrative business to AT&T, an already very
rich company. In the twelve months that ended November 30,
1960, AT&T set an all-time record for a corporation by earning
$1,244 million. The antitrust laws are a great variable in the
U.S. constitutional scheme of things. Since the laws were enacted
early in this century, the country has gone through periods of
vigorous enforcement and other periods when they fell into
virtual disuse. In 1960 and 1961, the pendulum was moving in
the direction of very strict enforcement.

If the solutions had been limited to those two, a long, bitter
controversy might have ensued. Joint ownership, however, occurred to a number of people in key positions as an excellent
solution. One of those particularly taken by the idea was Robert
G. Nunn Jr., a young attorney appointed by Glennan as a special assistant to work on policy problems related to the use of
communication satellite systems. Like Johnny Appleseed, Nunn
tramped all over Washington during the closing months of the
Eisenhower administration and the early months of the Kennedy administration, planting the idea wherever it was likely to
take root. "It was a disorderly process," Nunn commented wryly.

Another early advocate of joint ownership was Federal Communications Commissioner T. A. M. Craven, an old New Dealer
who was serving a second term on a 1956 appointment by President Eisenhower, after an absence of twelve years. Craven, who
had been the commission's chief engineer from 1935 to 1937
and a member from 1937 to 1944, prodded his colleagues to
face up to the problems involved in the new technology. He succeeded in persuading them to begin proceedings to solve them.

But before we get too deep into the policy problems, we had
better stop to define the various types of communication satellites. In the United States programs, they are divided into active
and passive satellites, high- and low-altitude satellites, and open
and secure communication systems.

An active communication satellite is essentially a radio receiver and transmitter in orbit. Because of its altitude, it fulfills the same function as a tall antenna tower—tall enough to transmit in a straight line beyond the curvature of the earth. A passive satellite is a simple reflector. The active satellite rebroadcasts the signal it receives from the ground. The passive satellite reflects it.

The "low"-altitude satellites are actually quite high. Altitudes vary from 1500 to 6000 miles for proposed operational systems. "High"-altitude is 22,300 miles. At that height, a satellite revolves around the earth in exactly twenty-four hours—at the same rate as the earth below it. If such a satellite is exactly over the equator and moves in an easterly direction, it will always be over the same spot on earth.

Security of military messages can be attained by carrying equipment for coding, or by delayed relay, in which the message is tape-recorded aboard the satellite on one side of the earth and replayed by command signal when it arrives over its intended receiver. Both methods require the addition of equipment aboard the satellite that is not needed in civilian communication systems. Thus the military satellites are more complex and expensive than those designed for civilian use.

The first communication satellite, called Project SCORE (Signal Communication Orbit Relay Experiment), was of the active type. An entire Atlas missile, put into orbit December 18, 1958, carried 150 pounds of equipment and demonstrated the possibility of voice communication from space by transmitting a Christmas greeting to the world from President Eisenhower. Messages were relayed both directly and on a delayed basis with tape replay.

SCORE was a project of the Defense Department and the Army. As a successor, they instituted Project Courier to launch more sophisticated communication devices. On October 4, 1960, the Army launched Courier I, a 500-pound satellite that carried 300 pounds of electronic gear including four transmitters, four receivers, five tape recorders, six antennas and special equipment for coding and decoding. The high-speed tape recorders were able to transmit, receive and store simultaneously about 68,000 coded words a minute. However, the satellite stopped transmitting after eighteen days.

The first passive communication satellite was the moon. In the late 1950s and early 1960s, U.S. scientists performed a whole series of experiments demonstrating the utility of the earth's natural satellite as a reflector of signals from the opposite side of the globe. It is even possible to hear signals bounced off the moon that were never intended to travel more than a short distance on earth.

On August 12, 1960, the civilian space agency launched Echo I, a 100-foot plastic balloon covered with a thin, highly reflecting layer of aluminum, which was inflated after it achieved its orbit about 1000 miles high. Echo demonstrated that it was equally possible to perform such experiments with an artificial satellite and, incidentally, provided highly visible evidence of U.S. activity in space. Echo was brighter than the North Star.

The twenty-four-hour communication satellite is one of many space flight ideas that originated in science fiction and now seems destined to become a reality. Arthur C. Clarke, whose fiction is probably the most scientific in the field, first proposed such a system in 1945. The twenty-four-hour satellite is so far up—its altitude is almost three times the earth's diameter—that it can "see" a much larger portion of the earth's surface than a satellite orbiting lower down. Also, the twenty-four-hour satellite is "fixed" in the sky, since it rotates at the same speed as the earth. Thus, a beam antenna could be pointed once at its direction in the sky and then left in that position. By contrast, a satellite in a lower orbit is moving constantly with respect to the earth below and covers a much smaller area. A system of three twenty-four-hour satellites should make it possible to relay communications between any two points on earth except for the areas around the North and South Poles, while between thirty and fifty satellites orbiting at lower altitudes might be required.

For the operational civil commercial satellite network, three types of satellites—high-altitude active, low-altitude active and low-altitude passive—are in competition. In addition, in Project Advent, the Defense Department and the Army are conducting research and development on a system at twenty-four-hour altitude designed to provide more secure communications than will be available from the commercial system. Even if a military satellite system should be established, however, the armed services will probably make considerable use of the commercial facilities for nonsecret messages, just as they do at present.

There is no agreement among scientists on which type of

system will be preferred for the commercial network. The passive satellite, such as Echo, has the great advantage of simplicity. It has no electronic components subject to failure in space. But it requires tremendous power in ground transmitters and extremely sensitive receivers. And it is limited to narrow bands of frequencies, too narrow for television relay unless very high power is used. The passive satellite is good only for telephone and telegraph communications. The low-altitude active satellite, on the other hand, might not have a very long life. Its route takes it through the heart of the earth's radiation belts; there was some question whether any electronic components could be expected to last long under such conditions. The high-altitude satellite might overcome the radiation problem, but developing the techniques for launching satellites into precise twenty-four-hour orbits is expected to take longer. Thus a twenty-four-hour system could not be developed as soon as one at low altitudes. Furthermore, the time required for relay of the message over a distance of 45,000 miles would cause a delay of a quarter-second in transmission, which might make it harder to suppress echoes in the voice signals. In view of these questions, NASA is sponsoring research in all three areas.

In 1960, however, when the potential applications of communication satellites first became apparent, the space agency was engaged in research only in passive satellites. In a 1958 agreement between NASA and the Defense Department, the armed services were to have jurisdiction over active satellites. AT&T, however, was convinced that low-altitude active satellites would provide the method by which it could develop a commercial system by the earliest possible date, and proposed to launch this type in its own experiments. To avoid letting a private company do all the research in that area, Glennan first had to get into position to perform some in his agency. The Defense Department agreed with him and on August 27, 1960, Deputy Defense Secretary James H. Douglas and Glennan signed an agreement under which NASA might develop active satellites specially designed for eventual civilian commercial use.

Next, the space agency needed money for experiments and authority from the administration to carry out such a program. Glennan took the proposal to the White House and President Eisenhower announced endorsement of the idea on January 1, 1961. Eisenhower directed NASA to take the lead within the

Executive Branch to advance the research and to apply its resources toward practical commercial application as early as possible. In his budget message January 16, Eisenhower asked Congress to appropriate $68 million for communication satellites, more than a third of which would be available as supplemental funds in the then-current 1961 budget year, so that work could begin as soon as possible. At the bottom of the 1962 budget sheet, however, there was an unusual entry: an income item of $10 million, representing an assumption that the government would receive that amount from private industry as payment for launching privately owned satellites. On January 19, the last full day of the Eisenhower administration, the Communications Commission authorized the AT&T request that a new frequency band be set aside for satellite communication.

The question was in limbo for several weeks after the change of administration. James E. Webb, President Kennedy's space administrator, did not assume office until February 14. Newton N. Minow, the new chairman of the FCC, was not sworn in until March 2. In the meantime, however, officials of the two agencies settled details of how they would work together and, on February 28, signed a memorandum of understanding. Communication satellites were at the top of Webb's list of priority problems, but he was not anxious to commit himself to a major policy decision on a complex matter quite so soon. Deputy Administrator Hugh L. Dryden offered to take responsibility for the agreement, by implication leaving the new administrator free to reverse the decision in the future if he so desired. Webb agreed to the arrangement. After full deliberation, he became convinced that the decision was correct.

The memorandum declared that the earliest practicable realization of a commercially operable communication satellite system is an urgent national objective. "In accordance with the traditional policy of conducting international communication services through private enterprise subject to governmental regulation," it continued, "private enterprise should be encouraged to undertake development and utilization of satellite systems for public communication services." Thus the transition between the Eisenhower and Kennedy administrations caused no more than a few weeks' delay in reaching and affirming a major national decision.

Some of the details, however, were scrutinized carefully by the new administration. As for the plan to make launching rockets available to AT&T, the first reaction was negative. The Democrats remembered well the charges of "giveaway" their party's spokesmen had made against the previous Republican administration. In addition, Webb, a former Under Secretary of State, felt intensely what a great advantage a communication satellite system would be to the United States in its international relations—a giant geopolitical factor, perhaps as important as the Panama and Suez Canals. He wanted to protect the government interest from the outset, regardless of whether private industry found operation of such a system economical. And so, on Webb's recommendation, Kennedy canceled the plan to depend on a $10 million payment in 1962 from private sources. In a message March 28, 1961, Kennedy asked Congress to appropriate the full cost of the research so that the government would retain full control "without prejudice to future arrangements for commercial operations." Webb said the change represented "a policy decision to have a good hard look at this before making commitments."

In the meantime, industry picked up the ball on the idea of a joint ownership venture. Less than a month after the new administration took office, the Lockheed Aircraft Corporation obtained preliminary assurances from the Department of Justice, headed by the President's brother, Robert Kennedy. Lee Loevinger, Assistant Attorney General in charge of the Antitrust Division, told Lockheed that the government would not proceed against such a combine under the criminal provisions of the antitrust laws, provided that the organizers kept the department informed of their actions on every step of the way.

The most important convert to the idea was a thirty-five-year-old Chicago lawyer who had been a partner of Adlai E. Stevenson until Kennedy named him as chairman of the Communications Commission. No one could suspect that Newton N. Minow was inordinately friendly with big business. He had hardly assumed office when he became embroiled in controversy with the major television networks over the quality of their programs. Starting without any preconceived notions, Minow went over the commission dockets and talked at length with Craven and the other commissioners and with Webb, Dryden and Nunn. He soon reached the conclusion that an industry "consortium" was the only solution. He called for industry and government agency comments by May 1 on how such a group might be organized.

The original Lockheed plan called for ownership of the central company by communications common carriers, equipment manufacturers and possibly the public at large. However, there were widely differing views in industry on the subject of who should and who should not be allowed to participate. The Department of Justice supported the idea of broad ownership, by both communication and equipment manufacturing companies.

In a first report on May 24, the Communications Commission came to the conclusion that the joint venture should be limited to existing common carriers of international telephone and telegraph communications. Minow said the inclusion of manufacturers would make the operation of the company cumbersome. He added that there are so many companies in the manufacturing business that it would be very difficult to determine eligibility.

AT&T had suggested that ownership of the venture should be apportioned by the amount of use a company makes of the system. On that basis, AT&T would own more than 80 per cent. The FCC refused to go along with that proposal. Minow said the commission was searching for a formula under which no single company could dominate.

Meanwhile, Kennedy approved a recommendation by Webb that more money be pumped into the research and development work, for maximum assurance that the operational system might be brought about as soon as possible. In his May 25, 1961, message to Congress, whose major proposal was manned flight to the moon, the President also requested an additional $50 million for communication satellites. In addition to increasing research, Webb planned to put some of the money into a fund that would make up part of the initial operating deficits of the commercial network. No one expects the system to operate at a profit for several years, perhaps not before the end of the decade. But if it is possible to make a choice of the best technical approach, Administrator Webb may call in the private owners and say to them, "Look here, the best estimate is that a communication satellite system can be established next year but it will operate with a net loss of X million dollars. The government can pay part of this with its available research and development funds. Can you put up the rest?"

In the research work, the passive communication satellite program continues with development of a larger, thicker-skinned balloon. Although Echo I successfully demonstrated that signals could be reflected from a satellite, its thin skin was penetrated by micrometeorites—tiny dust particles—in space and the inflating gas gradually leaked out over a period of months. As a result, the skin became wrinkled and the quality of the reflected signals degraded. For commercial operation, a satellite must retain high-quality reflected signals over a long period of time. The new Echo, to be launched beginning in 1962, was 135 feet in diameter instead of 100, to present a larger disk. The skin was stiffened by using two rather thick layers of aluminum foil instead of one thin one.

The space agency chose a contractor on May 18, 1961, to develop the first active repeater satellite with government funds under Project Relay. The Radio Corporation of America was chosen. After he had begun the government program, Webb told AT&T that he was ready to begin negotiations on providing rockets and launch services for that company's project, called Telstar or TSX. The negotiations produced a contract on July 27. Both Relay and TSX operate on the same general principles and both were to be launched during 1962. They differed in onboard equipment, the frequencies used and the general shape. There was also a slight difference in the orbital altitudes planned. Robert C. Seamans Jr., NASA associate administrator, says the duality of effort helps the national research program because many of the problems are statistical. For example, it isn't possible to predict the cost of a satellite system until the engineers know how long an individual electronic component will last in space, *on the average.* By flying as many satellites as possible, it will be possible to obtain more reliable estimates of average lifetimes.

In another NASA project, called SynCom, the Hughes Aircraft Company was authorized to develop a small active repeater satellite for use at the 22,300-mile altitude of a twenty-four-hour orbit. SynCom, however, will be launched into a twenty-four-hour *inclined* orbit, rather than one directly over the equator. It will be inclined at an angle of 33° to the equator. As a result, the satellite will revolve at the same rate as the earth but will not remain permanently over the equator. It will remain nearly above one meridian of longitude in the Atlantic Ocean, but will oscillate between the 33° parallels of north and south latitude. Achieving a twenty-four-hour inclined orbit is a less complicated guidance problem than going into the fixed position directly over the equator. Thus it was chosen as an interim experiment.

The first firing in the SynCom project, authorized August 10, 1961, was scheduled for late 1962. At about the same time, the military services planned to attempt a twenty-four-hour inclined orbit with the new Centaur rocket. A satellite called ARENTS (ARPA Experimental Test Satellite) was to test techniques and equipment that would be useful in the Army Advent program, which will develop a twenty-four-hour satellite to carry secure military communications. In addition, the ARENTS was to carry a "piggyback" NASA scientific satellite to obtain information on radiation levels 22,300 miles above the earth, so as to be able to predict the life of electronic components. The first Advent is to be flown after three ARENTS flights, probably in 1963.

The question of ownership of the operational commercial system will remain open for a while as research progresses, although the FCC gave the international communication carriers the first opportunity to attempt to organize a joint venture satisfactory to the government. On July 24, 1961, President Kennedy laid down a stringent set of stipulations in a policy statement prepared following lengthy consideration by the National Aeronautics and Space Council.

The system, Kennedy declared, must be truly global and not just serve profitable, high-volume routes such as across the North Atlantic. Ownership should be such that will assure maximum competition. Foreign participation must be possible. Access must be available for use by all authorized communication carriers. Competitive bidding or other effective competition must be assured in the purchase of equipment. The company must comply fully with antitrust laws and government regulations. An economic system should be developed, and benefits should be reflected in lower overseas communication rates.

The President committed the United States to give maximum assurance of rapid scientific and technical progress by supporting research and development, to control all U.S. launchings and to use the commercial system for general governmental purposes, when in the national interest. He said also that the United States would assure the effective use of the radio frequency spectrum, provide technical aid to newly developing countries to bring them into the system and examine with other countries how the United Nations and its specialized agency, the International Telecommunications Union, can play a constructive role.

If a private venture meeting those standards can be organized promptly enough, the communication satellite system will be in private hands, just as is the rest of the American communication industry. But if private enterprise is unwilling or unable to do so, the government may have to move in. "I am anxious," Kennedy said, "that development of this new technology . . . proceed with all possible promptness."

13. WEATHER SATELLITES

EVERY MAN who has ever tried to describe the weather has been in a predicament similar to that of the blind men confronted with an elephant—he could perceive only a small portion. Six million billion tons of air surround our planet—hot in some places, cold in others; clouded here, clear there; usually moving, occasionally still. But altogether, the atmosphere is one great heat engine. The weather at the North Pole is related to that over the equator, for both are part of a single system. If it were only possible to know what the weather is doing all over the earth now, it would be a simpler problem than it is to predict what will happen tomorrow.

Furthermore, if scientists knew both what the weather is doing and why, it might be possible—at least in some cases—to control it. Weather control is a seemingly hopeless project for the present because of the vast amount of energy involved in even a small storm—greater than that of the largest hydrogen bomb. But Francis W. Reichelderfer, chief of the U.S. Weather Bureau, believes that with knowledge about the beginning stages of storms, it is conceivable that relatively small forces might be used to deflect them or break them into smaller disturbances. "Take tornadoes," Reichelderfer told me. "They may occur in such a random way that we can do nothing about them. But maybe a mechanism we haven't discovered will be a key to preventing them or reducing their violence."

As long as the meteorologist is limited to the earth, he has only a gnat's-eye view of the weather. He knows what is happening only in a small area around his station. He is in touch with other stations in his own country and, indirectly, with stations around the world. But he knows nothing of what goes on between stations. Furthermore, almost all weather stations are concentrated in the land regions, which make up about 30 per cent of the earth's surface. From the remaining four-fifths, weather information is sparse or nonexistent. Since storms and major weather systems often develop over great stretches of ocean, the only information comes from ships and planes passing through. For huge areas off the shipping and air lanes, there is no information at all for long periods of time.

From a satellite, the weather man can see the whole elephant. The Tiros weather satellites, which televised pictures to ground stations, enabled forecasters to see cloud formations up to 1000 miles long. By patching pictures together, it was possible to produce a panorama extending all the way across an ocean. "With Tiros, we get a moon's-eye view," Reichelderfer commented. "We didn't realize how significant it would be."

The first weather satellites were experiments. Tiros I, launched from Cape Canaveral April 1, 1960, was merely intended to accomplish two goals: first, to demonstrate that it is possible to take pictures of the earth's cloud cover from space and to get them into the hands of meteorologists fast enough so they will be of value in weather forecasting; second, to obtain pictures that will help scientists understand more about the workings of the weather, to improve weather forecasting and thus, perhaps, to develop theories relating to weather control. But in addition to achieving those goals, the satellite produced a wealth of information that was of immediate value in day-to-day forecasting. During its first few weeks, Tiros demonstrated the potential of satellites by taking pictures of a tropical cyclone and a towering bank of clouds that spawned tornadoes in Texas and Oklahoma.

Weather information is of value for many reasons. The transportation industry needs short-term forecasts in great detail so as to move people and goods safely. Accurate information is of obvious importance for any nation's defense. The public wants weather forecasts mostly for convenience—but sometimes lives and property are at stake.

If long-term forecasts could be made available, however, profound benefits would ensue. Accurate, seasonal weather predictions several months in advance could take most of the guessing out of agriculture. Knowing whether next winter will be hard or easy is equally valuable to industry—producers of overshoes and tire chains, to take an obvious example. Under Secretary of Commerce Edward Gudeman, a former Sears Roebuck vice president, believes accurate, long-range forecasts would make it possible to substantially reduce periodic unemployment in industries producing such seasonal goods.

There is a long history of world cooperation in the exchange of weather information. In 1878, the world's weather services formed the International Meteorological Organization, which was reconstituted in 1950 as the World Meteorological Organization, a specialized agency of the United Nations. Regardless of the temperature of the cold war and other international tensions, weather information flows back and forth across national borders all over the world on a regular basis. The WMO provides an obvious vehicle for the exchange of data gathered by weather satellites, when the time comes to set up an international system.

Although the first weather satellites were American, Russia developed interest too. In the fall of 1960, about six months after the launching of the first Tiros, a Soviet scientist proposed a worldwide system of weather satellites. In an article distributed to publications in the United States by the Soviet Embassy, Professor Georgi I. Pokrovsky estimated that about half the farm produce lost because of crop failures could be saved if long-term forecasts were made possible by weather satellites. He put the annual savings in money at 500 billion rubles, which he said was many times the total spent on rocketry throughout the world. "A worldwide system is a 'must,'" Professor Pokrovsky said, "for it is impossible to forecast weather separately for the Soviet Union or the United States, nor even separately for Eurasia or America. Such a system should become a joint project for all countries." However, Pokrovsky apparently spoke only for himself. There was no firm indication that the Soviet government shared his view.

Three months later, in his first State of the Union message, President Kennedy made a similar proposal. Noting that the United States was "ahead in the science and technology of space while the Soviet Union is ahead in the capacity to lift large vehicles into orbit," Kennedy invited all nations, including the Soviet Union, to join together in such peaceful endeavors as weather prediction by satellite. The proposal began to bear fruit in May, 1961, at a Geneva meeting of the executive council of the UN World Meteorological Organization. Reichelderfer and his Soviet counterpart, Andrei A. Zolotouhin, talked privately at length about how such a system might work. It was the first time a Soviet representative had been willing even to discuss an international weather satellite system. Previously, Soviet representatives had rebuffed U.S. suggestions of cooperation on the ground that they constituted a "cover" for the development of reconnaissance satellites. And the Soviet government refused to take part in an international program in the summer of 1961 designed to exploit pictures taken by Tiros III.

Perhaps a word is in order here about the technical difference between weather and reconnaissance satellites. The first two Tiros weather satellites had two types of cameras, with wide- and narrow-angle lenses. The wide-angle lens took pictures 800 to 1200 miles on a side, with resolution of one and a half to two miles. The narrow-angle camera took pictures 80 to 100 miles on a side, with resolution of about a sixth of a mile. Even the narrow-angle pictures had too little resolution to show information of military value. But some later U.S. weather satellites, beginning with the third Tiros, did not even have the resolving capacity of the narrow-angle lens. To make certain that broad coverage would be available, both cameras on the third Tiros had wide-angle lenses. In its Samos satellite program, the U.S. Air Force is attempting to develop cameras and related equipment that will obtain information of military value. The details of the Samos cameras are a military secret, but it stands to reason that much finer resolution than produced by even the narrow-angle camera on Tiros will be necessary. If Soviet scientists have any doubt on this score, they can examine the engineering details of the Tiros cameras, which have been made fully public.

But regardless of whether the Soviet Union cooperates, the United States is going ahead on its own with the establishment of a system of weather satellites. It will cost about $60 million a year, in addition to research and development expenditures, to operate the system. The U.S. government has decided that the benefits to the United States alone are well worth that much money. Hurricanes hit the East and Gulf coasts every summer and fall. With satellites, the exact course of a hurricane can be followed and people in threatened coastal areas can be warned in time to get out. "Drowning is the greatest danger from hurricanes and typhoons," Reichelderfer says. "Very few deaths are caused by the blast of the wind itself." A few years ago thousands of persons were drowned by giant waves that swept ashore with two typhoons in East Pakistan. With six hours' warning—which could have been provided easily with a satellite system—most of the lives could have been saved.

Like many applications of space exploration, the idea of weather satellites originated in science fiction. The first serious proposal, however, was put forth by the Rand Corporation in a secret document for the Air Force in 1951. Harry Wexler, the Weather Bureau's director of meteorological research, made the idea public in a talk at Philadelphia in 1954. He spoke a few months before an Aerobee rocket, launched from White Sands, New Mexico, photographed a well-developed storm center that was responsible for widespread flash floods in the southwestern United States and later in Chicago, although the conventional network of surface weather stations gave only slight indication of the storm.

Project TIROS (Television and Infra Red Observation Satellite) began in April, 1958, when the Defense Department's Advanced Research Projects Agency began a multiservice program to investigate the use of television as an instrument aboard a satellite to obtain weather information. In December, 1958, the project was ordered transferred to the National Aeronautics and Space Administration, effective in the spring of 1959.

The first weather satellite was launched April 1, 1960. Its orbit, inclined at 48.3° to the equator, carried it over all parts of the earth between the 48.3° parallels of latitude during the seventy-eight days that its television gear remained in operation. Altogether, 22,952 cloud-cover pictures, more than 60 per cent of good quality, were transmitted to the ground.

On April 10, Tiros I gave man his first look at a fully developed tropical storm. The camera with the wide-angle lens recorded the cyclone, 800 miles east of Brisbane, Australia. A month later, the weather satellite photographed a very bright square cloud mass from which a series of tornadoes and hailstorms developed near the Texas-Oklahoma line about two hours later. Only by a stroke of luck was the cloud mass identified—during detailed analysis several weeks after the event of May 19. But David S. Johnson, chief of the Bureau's satellite

Laboratory, believes that in the future it will be possible to warn of the possible approach of tornadoes when unusual cloud masses are detected.

The Tiros picture revealed a remarkable degree of organization in the cloud systems over most of the earth's surface, particularly the ocean regions. Weather men confirmed a notion that had previously been just a theory, that the spiral, banded structure of tropical storms also exists outside the tropics. The tropical storm may be a few hundred to a thousand miles in diameter. Outside the tropics, the spiral formation may spread across an entire ocean. The larger the formation, the less violent the winds, meteorologists found. Nevertheless, it is now clear that the whole system can be considered as a unit.

On land, things are not so simple. Mountains, large lakes and variations in surface absorption and reflection of the sun's heat complicate the situation in ways that make understanding much more difficult. But the weather men are confident that, with continued research, they will obtain the answers there too. The satellite is of course only one tool for learning about basic weather processes. Surface observations, rocket and balloon soundings, optical measurements, scattering of radio waves and observation of meteor trails provide means of determining what the atmosphere is doing in great detail. But satellite observations make it possible to tie the details together—to see the woods as well as individual trees.

Television is not the only form of satellite instrumentation that can help to observe and understand the weather. Another important measurement is the radiation that comes from the earth. If meteorologists can determine the amount of heat energy received from the sun, and the amount the earth reflects and radiates back to space, they can establish by simple subtraction the amount of heat received in any given area. The amount of heat radiated out into space varies according to its wavelength, the nature of the surface, the amount and type of clouds and the composition of the atmosphere, which is like the glass roof of a greenhouse. It is transparent and lets in visible light, which heats the surface. The surface reflects some of the visible light back to space and radiates some of the energy in the infrared wavelengths, which are absorbed by the atmosphere. Thus part of the sun's energy remains on earth.

I should point out here that every object emits some sort of electromagnetic radiation. The distribution of wavelengths is determined by the temperature. The sun, being very hot, emits radiation in the short, ultraviolet and visible wavelengths. The surface of the earth, being cooler, emits radiation in the longer-wave infrared region. The temperature of any body can be determined from afar by measuring the relative intensity of its radiation in various wavelengths.

Tiny changes in atmospheric composition can bring about marked variations in the greenhouse effect. Carbon dioxide and water vapor, each of which makes up only a fraction of one per cent of the atmosphere, are strong absorbers of infrared. A slight change in either can change the greenhouse effect greatly, and thus affect the local weather. If the air is dry, for example, it will not absorb as much infrared radiation. Thus the temperature drops much more rapidly at night in a dry climate because the earth radiates its heat out into space with less interference.

Measurements of heat radiation provide meteorologists with information that sheds important light on weather processes. If possible, of course, they obtain the information on the surface. During the International Geophysical Year, United States scientists measured heat received from the sun and radiated back at six Antarctic stations, two in the Arctic and on Mauna Loa, a mountain in Hawaii. But for the big picture, satellite measurements are required.

The first attempt to obtain information from space on the earth's radiation consisted of a pair of photoelectric cells aboard the satellite Vanguard II, launched February 17, 1959. They were designed to make a rough measurement of the total cloud cover of the earth, rather than pinpoint information for specific areas. The satellite achieved orbit and separated from the final-stage rocket. But after separation, the rocket caught fire in a final burst, struck the satellite and introduced a wobbling motion. Since the scientists on the ground did not know just how it was wobbling, they were unable to interpret the data transmitted.

The next attempt was much more successful. Explorer VII, launched October 13, 1959, carried an elaborate radiation balance experiment designed by Verner E. Suomi of the University of Wisconsin. It produced a great deal of information that Suomi was able to relate to the distribution of cloud cover. In areas where the clouds were deep or at high altitude, the heat loss from the earth was low. Where there were no clouds, a great deal of heat was radiated. Thus, with infrared measurements, he showed that it is possible to "see" the cloud cover at night, while television can of course be used only on the daytime side of the earth.

Originally, the space agency planned to install infrared measuring equipment on the first Tiros, hence the name, whose letters stand for Television and Infra Red Observation Satellite. But the infrared gear was not ready on time, and so the first was launched without it. But when Tiros II was launched November 23, 1960, it carried instruments designed to measure infrared and visible radiation in five wavelength bands.*

The five channels were designed to provide facts that could be cross-checked against each other and against the information from the televised pictures. Physicists reported that the most interesting information came through a channel of wavelengths that water vapor does not readily absorb, a "water vapor window" from 8 to 12 microns. Since such radiation is not heavily absorbed, it provides a comparatively accurate measure of the temperature at the earth's surface or at the top of a cloud formation. A sudden drop in the temperature recorded as the satellite moves from one area to another probably represents the beginning of a clouded region. Thus the 8-12 micron channel is apparently best suited for measuring cloud cover on the night side of the earth. It also may be possible to make rough estimates of cloud heights. If the surface temperatures are known from measurements of clear areas, the amount of the temperature drop indicates roughly the height of the cloud, something that can be very valuable in predicting tornadoes. It is known that most tornadoes spring from cumulonimbus cloud formations much taller than normal—usually between 30,000 and 40,000 feet, and sometimes even taller. Meteorologists are continuing to study the infrared data from Tiros II and its successors with the hope that they may be able to distinguish demarcations between

* The five: (1) Wavelength of 6.3 microns (a micron is 1/10,000 centimeter) to detect radiation from the upper layers of the atmospheric water vapor; (2) Total emitted in wavelengths between 7 and 30 microns, like part of the Suomi experiment on Explorer VII; (3) Reflection from the earth in the visible and near infrared and ultraviolet, between 0.2 and 6 microns, (visible range—0.4-0.7 microns); (4) 8-12 microns, the so-called water vapor window; (5) visible light between 0.55 and 0.75 microns.

snow and open ground, and the edges of ocean currents. Many other applications of radiation data may be possible.

The Tiros satellites have two important limitations. First, their orbits are inclined about 48° to the equator, which means that they view only the region of the earth approximately between the 55° parallels of latitude. They do not reach any point north of 48° north latitude or south of 48° south latitude. The limitation is due to the fact that they are launched from Cape Canaveral. Satellites can be launched from Cape Canaveral within a fan of directions extending from southeast to northeast. For an orbit over or near the poles, it is ordinarily necessary to launch in a north or south direction.* This is forbidden at Cape Canaveral for safety reasons. Such a trajectory would carry the rocket over populated land areas. The United States has a launching site for polar and near-polar orbits just north of Point Arguello, California, about 150 miles north of Los Angeles. A launching due south from Point Arguello travels over more than 8000 miles of the Pacific Ocean before crossing land at Antarctica. But the Tiros satellites were launched by Thor-Able and Thor-Delta rockets, for which there were no launching facilities on the Pacific Coast.

The second limitation to Tiros satellites is caused by their orientation in space. To maintain stability, they spin at a rate of 9 to 12 revolutions per minute. If the spin slows down, scientists speed it by sending a radio signal that commands the firing of a pair of tiny solid-propellant rockets mounted on the outer rim of the Tiros. Like a gyroscope, the satellite remains spinning with its axis always oriented in the same direction. Thus, as it revolves around the earth, the cameras are sometimes pointed toward the earth, sometimes at an angle and much of the time out into space. The cameras are in position to see the earth only part of the time.

To overcome the limitations of the Tiros satellites, the space agency began development of Nimbus, a more sophisticated weather satellite, which is designed to fit into an operational system. Nimbus is intended to fly in an orbit inclined at about

---

* Another method is "dog leg" firing of an upper stage after a coast period that carries it out over the ocean. But this expends energy and would require a larger booster rocket for any given weight in orbit.

80° to the equator, 10° off from polar, and will thus reach almost to the North and South Poles and be able to see practically all of the earth at one time or another. Nimbus will be launched by Thor-Agena B rockets down the Pacific Missile Range. It will have movable spinning wheels and gas jets to control its attitude in space so that its cameras and other equipment always point toward the earth. Since the Thor-Agena is more powerful than the Thor-Delta, Nimbus can weigh considerably more—upward of 600 pounds compared with 280 for Tiros. Much of the weight will be taken up by the attitude control gear, but there will be more instruments too.

Nimbus will be launched in the middle of the night. It will fly south over the Pacific and Antarctica and rise in the Eastern Hemisphere at exactly noon, local time. The 80° inclination of its orbit will be retrograde—that is, as it flies north or south it will also move from east to west at the same apparent rate as the sun. An imaginary line between the centers of the sun and the earth is within the plane of the Nimbus orbit. When Nimbus crosses the equator on the sunlit side of the earth it will always be noon, local time, on the surface below. On the opposite side, the time will always be midnight.

If the orbit were exactly polar, such a situation would prevail only on the first day after the launching. For as the earth revolves around the sun, the sun appears to move. The satellite, whirling about the earth like a gyroscope, tends to remain in a plane oriented in the same direction. Although the imaginary earth-sun line is in that plane the first day, the line gradually leaves the plane of the orbit as the days go by, so that the time is no longer noon when Nimbus is over the equator, but a little earlier each day. Three months later, after the earth had moved a quarter of the way around the sun, the satellite would cross the equator at dawn. The imaginary earth-sun line would now be perpendicular to the orbit plane. The diagram on page 172 will show what I mean.

But the mathematicians have worked out a clever trick to keep the orbit plane lined up with the sun, so that the noontime passages will continue around the year. The trick is based on two facts—the precession of gyroscopes and the bulge of the earth at the equator. Precession is something very difficult to visualize

NIMBUS orbit

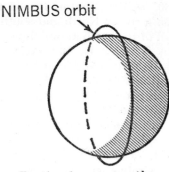

Earth, three months
after launch

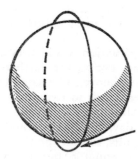

Earth on date of
launching NIMBUS

NIMBUS orbit

unless you have seen it. But it is usually demonstrated in high
school science classes.

The demonstrations show that when we attempt to tilt a gyroscope in one direction, it actually tilts in another direction, at
right angles to the direction of the force applied. The effect of
the earth's equatorial bulge is even harder to visualize. On the
surface of the earth, because of the bulge, the force of gravity
is slightly greater at the poles than at the equator. In a perfectly circular orbit about the poles, the situation would be just
the opposite. The attraction would be less when the satellite
was over the poles, because it would be a little farther away. In

an inclined orbit, the slight changes in gravitational attraction that take place have a tendency to tilt the orbital plane. The tilting introduces precession, which has been observed in the orbits of all satellites launched since 1957. The mathematical trick is to use the built-in precession in a way that will help accomplish the Nimbus mission of staying permanently in an orbit in the same plane as the earth-sun line. For an orbit inclined about 80°, the mathematicians have calculated that precession will keep the orbit pointed toward the sun if a satellite is at about 600 miles altitude.

Four launchings are planned in the research and development program for the Nimbus satellite, over a period extending from 1962 to 1964. The first two in the series will have television cameras for daytime observation, infrared instruments for observing clouds at night and possibly some instruments designed to measure the radiation in various wavelengths that comes from the sun. The primary purpose of the early flights, however, will be to prove out the techniques of achieving circular orbit in the precise inclination and altitude necessary for the proper rate of precession, and maintaining satellite attitude so that the satellite instruments always point toward the earth.

For the later launchings, new instruments will be installed. One is radar, which has proved a tremendous success aboard commercial aircraft for helping pilots steer around stormy areas. Radar, which is simply a powerful radio beacon transmitting in the microwave frequencies, detects distant objects by receiving reflections of its own signal. It finds bad weather by observing signals bounced off the falling raindrops. On a satellite, radar equipment could spot and follow storms long before they come within range of airborne and surface instruments. It would operate night and day and would tell whether rain is actually falling, thus carrying out tasks that cannot be accomplished with cloud-cover photography.

Another fascinating form of instrument is the infrared spectrometer. Under an ingenious plan devised by L. D. Kaplan of Massachusetts Institute of Technology, the Weather Bureau's scientists believe it might be possible to obtain exact measurements of the temperature at several altitudes in the atmosphere. Kaplan proposes to use a spectrometer—a device like a glass prism—to separate the infrared "light" from the atmosphere into several wavelengths in the neighborhood of 15 microns, a wavelength at which the carbon dioxide in the atmosphere radiates fairly strongly. On the assumption that carbon dioxide is mixed in the atmosphere at a known rate, Kaplan suggests that by solving a series of mathematical equations temperatures can be obtained for the atmosphere at different altitudes. In a paper published in 1959 in a scientific journal,* he suggested using ten measurements, which would yield temperatures at ten altitudes. The Weather Bureau decided this would be too complex, at least for the early experiments, and settled for four, at wavelengths that would reveal temperatures at four altitudes above the tops of almost all clouds.

The Nimbus will have six television cameras in two sets of three. The cameras will look down to the earth in a fanlike configuration, one straight down, one at an angle to the left of the orbital path and one at an angle to the right. The second set will be a reserve, in case of failure in the cameras of the first set. There may be a half-dozen ordinary infrared measurements, radar, infrared spectrometer and several earth-sun experiments. Thus Nimbus will be producing a fantastic amount of information—which must be processed and delivered quickly if it is to be of operational value. Communication satellites may provide a means to deliver data. But there may be so much data that delivery could occupy as much bandwidth as a television channel, making the cost astronomical.

Morris Tepper, the space agency's chief of meteorological programs, would like to develop some sort of device for analysis of satellite observations on board the satellite, so as to reduce the volume of data sent to the ground. NASA is sponsoring research on the whole problem of data transmission from the satellite to the final user.

Beyond the Nimbus, the space agency has plans for a weather satellite in a twenty-four-hour equatorial orbit, like the SynCom communication satellite mentioned in the previous chapter. The twenty-four-hour weather satellite, called Aeros, will have the job of following a particular storm area continuously with the use of a Zoomar-type lens. The telescope-type lens is necessary because the satellite will be 22,300 miles from the earth. Aeros

*Journal of the Optical Society of America, Vol. 49, pp. 1004-1007.

will be very much like Nimbus in general configuration, except for the addition of a rocket designed to provide short bursts of propulsion to correct deviations from its orbit. The first Aeros satellites are to be launched in the 1964-65 period.

Continuous improvement in the capability and the sophistication of weather satellites will be taking place during much of the decade. Nimbus will be a great improvement over Tiros. The later Nimbus will be able to perform more tasks than the early version. And with Aeros added to the Nimbus satellites, the system will reach the ultimate that we can now foresee. But weather forecasters are not willing to wait five years or more for a sophisticated system when the system available now will do a great deal of work for them.

The original NASA plan was to launch three Tiros satellites in the 1960-61 period for research purposes to gain experience. But the weather services found the Tiros information so useful that they began pressing, soon after the first launching, for an extension of the program that would enable them to make maximum operational use of the data. The space agency's scientists maintained that it was not economical to set up an elaborate organization to use Tiros operationally, when Nimbus would be coming along soon. To work out a plan for an operational system, a committee was formed with a jawbreaking title, the Panel on Meteorological Satellites, National Coordinating Committee for Aviation Meteorology, which worked out a plan between December, 1960, and April, 1961. With only slight modifications, President Kennedy approved the program and recommended Congressional action the following month.

The new program called for addition of three Tiros satellites —to make a total of six—before the beginning of the operational system with the first Nimbus launching in late 1962. The operational system broke down into three phases: from mid-1962 through 1963, 1964 and 1965, and 1966 on. In the first phase, a single Nimbus will be in orbit most or all of the time. In the second phase, one will be in orbit all the time and at the end of the phase, two will be in orbit most of the time. In the third phase, two will be in orbit all of the time. With the beginning of the second phase, when two satellites are in orbit at the same time, the Nimbus satellites will be launched in a different plane. Instead of a noontime orbit the next Nimbus will circle the

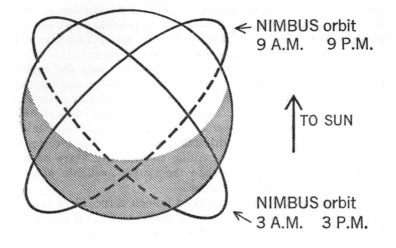

← NIMBUS orbit
9 A.M.   9 P.M.

↑ TO SUN

NIMBUS orbit
↖ 3 A.M.   3 P.M.

Earth, viewed from above North Pole

earth in a plane inclined at 45° to the imaginary line between the earth and the sun, so that the time is always 9 A.M. or 9 P.M. local time when it crosses the equator. The second satellite will be in a 3 A.M.-3 P.M. orbit, at right angles to the 9 A.M.-9 P.M. orbit. The diagram will illustrate the situation.

The primary radio command and data-collection station for the first Nimbus satellites will be at Fairbanks, Alaska, under the operational plan. It will be part of a major space tracking station the space agency began building in late 1960. Since Fairbanks is north of the Arctic Circle, a satellite in a near-polar orbit will be in view on more than half of the orbits. A second U.S. station will be in the northeastern United States, at a site to be chosen. There probably will be a third station in northwestern Europe, if a European country or countries are interested in establishing one. The cost, however, is a major factor in building foreign stations. Depending on local conditions, a station can cost as much as several million dollars or the equivalent in local currency.

In all likelihood, only a few of the more well-to-do countries of the world will be able to afford fully equipped receiving stations, even if they band together on a regional basis. And if the same data were to be transmitted to more than one station, the equipment aboard the satellite would have to be much more complex. A solution suggested by Harry Wexler, the Weather Bureau research chief, is the continuous transmission of some data, such as local cloud pictures, leaving the remainder to be processed at a central location. From the central location, information would then be chosen and distributed to countries all over the world at their expense, in whatever detail they want. Here is where the communication satellite network will probably fit into the operation. The cost of transmitting the message, whether by satellite or conventional facilities, will provide strong incentive for keeping the message short. Distribution of cloud-cover information from Tiros II provided an example of what might happen. The U.S. military services transmitted cloud-cover analyses to Europe by radio facsimile and British and German weather stations also copied the message. The southern half of the world, however, received its information in word form. The U.S. Weather Bureau sent regular messages to the International Antarctic Analysis Center in Melbourne, Australia, whence they were relayed to the Australian weather bureau.

Even with perfect international relations, Wexler believes that international funding of launchings would be completely impractical. "Each launching nation should fund its own launchings and give notice of launchings, with necessary instructions for readout," he says. "If there were any U.S.-Soviet agreement, it might be to use the same frequencies and similar instruments and to launch in coordinated orbits for optimum coverage."

14. AT HOME AND ABROAD

AMERICA'S ECONOMIC WELL-BEING depends on federal expenditure, of which more than half goes for defense. One of every ten jobs in the United States is in the armed forces, on the civilian staff of the Defense Department or in defense industry. Three times during his eight years in office, President Eisenhower moved to cut defense spending or at least to hold it in check. Three recessions followed—in 1953-54, 1957-58 and 1961. The 1953 cutback followed the Korean armistice. The 1957 reduction took place because the federal debt was approaching too close to the ceiling set by the law. The downturn of 1960-61 occurred while the defense budget was actually rising; only the *rate* of increase had slowed.

Even while government spending increases, recession can occur because the nation's population and labor force may be growing even more rapidly—as was the case in 1960-61—and because technological progress may reduce industry's needs for manpower. At the end of World War II, Franklin D. Roosevelt's goal of sixty million jobs was a symbol of full employment. Today, full employment would require more than seventy million; the required total rises daily. Meanwhile, U.S. industry, steadily becoming more automated, produces more with fewer employees. Such productive efficiency is essential if America is to keep prices down—both to avoid inflation at home and to compete effectively in foreign markets. But a constant supply of new jobs must be forthcoming if widespread unemployment is to be avoided. As the Red Queen told Alice, "It takes all the running you can do to keep in the same place; if you want to get somewhere else, you have to run twice as fast as that."

Since World War II, the requirements of national defense have supplied the new jobs. A $40 billion defense budget in 1960 employed about three million federal employees and three and a half million in defense industry. The $46 billion defense budget of 1962 employed an even greater proportion. The strategic systems—missiles, bombers, Polaris submarines, radar warning and military spacecraft—have the greatest impact on the civilian economy. The Air Force enjoys by far the largest military procurement budget, and a large part of Navy procurement is for the strategic Polaris system. Conventional warfare requires Army and Navy manpower, whose weapons are produced to a fairly large extent in government arsenals. Thus economic benefits flow at a much greater rate from expenditures on strategic systems. When the defense budget is formed, economic considerations exert powerful pressures on their behalf, both in the Executive Branch and in Congress.

During 1958 and 1959, the economic pressures had the beneficial effect of spurring vital missile development. Russia had conducted successful tests of her first intercontinental ballistic missile in the summer of 1957, and it was apparently ready for installation not long thereafter. The United States did not conduct a full-range flight of the Atlas, its first ICBM, until November, 1958, and the first combat installation was not completed until September, 1959. Thus a gap of fifteen months existed between the development of the Soviet and U.S. programs. During the early years of the ICBM, the United States overcame the gap with preponderant bomber strength and with shorter-range missiles in Britain, Italy, Turkey and other allied nations. Later, America began to outproduce Russia in ICBMs.

Any doubt about U.S. strategic superiority in the missile age was dispelled, however, in the fall of 1960, when the first of the Polaris submarines went into operation. The missile gap is now a thing of the past. Before Polaris tipped the balance, it might have been theoretically possible for a rain of Soviet missiles, aimed three or more at every target, to destroy all U.S. land missiles and air bases and surface ships at sea. Whether the Soviet economy could stand the strain of producing that many ICBMs was another question, of course. It was theoretically conceivable. But the Polaris is a relatively invulnerable strategic weapon. Even if antisubmarine forces can occasionally find and destroy a submarine, their mobility makes it manifestly impossible to destroy America's Polaris fleet in a simultaneous surprise strike.

Up to 1961, Congress authorized the Navy to produce twenty-nine submarines, each carrying sixteen Polaris missiles with yield of about one megaton (the equivalent of a million tons of TNT). The Air Force was authorized to produce 600 Minuteman missiles carrying one-megaton warheads, 129 Atlas missiles and 108 Titan missiles, each carrying a warhead of about five megatons. By 1965, that program called for the United States to have an ICBM and Polaris strategic force of almost 2000 megatons, enough to lay waste broad areas of the Soviet Union and China without the use of a single bomber or short-range missile on allied soil. Up to 1965, as the missile force builds up, America's great preponderance in strategic bomber strength, combined with missiles on allied bases, will maintain an equally powerful strategic position.

Thus it is clear that the United States may well have more strategic power than is necessary to deter a surprise Soviet nuclear attack, while American conventional forces are just as clearly insufficient to deal with the worldwide threat of smaller-scale war. This is the situation that makes desirable a U.S. agreement with the Soviet Union on a reduction of strategic arms—why we can disarm even as we arm. The Soviet Union has equally good reasons for desiring disarmament. Arms production is a burden, not a stimulus, to the Soviet economy. If Khrushchev really means to build up the Soviet standard of living as promised by the 1961 Communist Party congress, he must cut back on defense. Furthermore, both the United States and the Soviet Union are under strong disarmament pressure from world opinion.

But with strategic arms production essential to U.S. economic health, how can the nation afford to cut back? The answer usually given is that experience at the end of World War II showed reconversion to peacetime economic activity to be no insuperable problem and that, in any case, disarmament would take place in gradual stages. Also, producing the inspection equipment would generate economic activity. Some specialists have suggested timetables as long as ten years, so that the U.S. economy can gradually absorb the economic effects. But the

World War II analogy is almost wholly irrelevant to the present situation. A huge backlog of civilian demand had been developed by wartime shortages, which do not exist today. Industry was kept busy for several years to satisfy the pent-up demand. Moreover, Khrushchev would never agree to disarmament in such gradual stages, for American convenience, to help avoid a recession. Why should he? His motive for entering a disarmament agreement is to lift a heavy burden from the Soviet economy, the sooner the better. He starts from a position of demanding immediate, general and complete disarmament. While we may hope he will modify that position in negotiations, nevertheless we must assume that any agreement acceptable to the Soviet Union must provide for disarmament at a fairly rapid pace.

There are shortages in the American economy that could fill the gap; schools, teachers, urban and suburban transportation, apartment housing, local police, youth workers and a dozen other categories of service traditionally performed by local and state government might be mentioned. It may be technically both desirable and feasible to build up such public services to take up the disarmament slack. But the task is almost impossible politically. Even with the most vocal public support for such a program, fifty state legislatures and hundreds of local governments would not act in unison to create the new jobs. Many could not do so if they wanted; they have long since exhausted their tax resources. Huge new federal aid programs will provide the only practical means of financing. President Kennedy, who achieved considerable legislative success in his first year, probably will be able to persuade Congress to adopt many such programs. But it will almost certainly be impossible to adopt them soon enough to equalize the economic effect of disarmament. The new programs will run afoul of too many entrenched interests to be passed quickly, and additional delays will result from the time needed for action on the state and local levels to take advantage of federal aid.

An even more difficult political hurdle will be determined resistance by the military services and the defense industry. "This conjunction of an immense military establishment and a large arms industry is new in the American experience," President Eisenhower noted in his final speech to the nation on January 17, 1961. "The total influence—economic, political, even spiritual—is felt in every city, every statehouse, every office of the Federal government. We recognize the imperative need for this development. Yet we must not fail to comprehend its grave implications. Our toil, resources and livelihood are all involved; so is the very structure of our society.

"In the councils of government," Eisenhower continued, "we must guard against the acquisition of unwarranted influence, whether sought or unsought, by the military-industrial complex. The potential for the disastrous rise of misplaced power exists and will persist."

Under civilian direction, the expedition to the moon can fill the economic gap and without encouraging growth of unwarranted military influence. Space contracts can be placed with the very same plants whose defense contracts are to be cut off. If the government coordinates its actions, no unemployment need occur at all in such plants. And the space project in question has the benefit of an established team of managers and engineers, rather than having to go through the time-consuming task of recruiting and organizing.

The only weakness of using space as an economic equalizer is that it may be too small. In the first six years of the decade, the Kennedy administration expects to obligate between $28 and $30 billion on the combined civilian-military space program, rising steadily from $1.78 billion in the year ended June 30, 1961, to perhaps $6½ billion in the year ending June 30, 1966. About two-thirds of the total will go for the lunar landing venture. Even $6½ billion, however, is small potatoes in comparison with a $46 billion total defense budget. The question is not whether America can afford the moon program, as some conservatives put it, but whether it is big enough to fill the economic gap. The other nonmilitary programs will have to build up quickly too.

The lunar expedition can assume another burden that has been carried by the defense effort. "About a tenth of the goods comprising the gross national product," says Senator Robert S. Kerr, "represent new designs, model change-overs or recent evolutionary changes resulting from research and development." Before World War II, the nation spent less than a billion dollars a year on research and development. By 1961, the annual total was $13 billion, of which $8 billion was supplied by the Federal government, almost all of it for military purposes.

If left to their own resources, only the wealthiest private

corporations can afford to support basic research. Even applied research is limited in most companies to product improvement. But with the government paying the cost of research and new technology, industry has been able to feed it back into civilian applications at a rapid rate. Ironically, military research has paid the cost of most technological change in civilian industry since World War II. The moon expedition, which also will involve spending huge sums for research and development, provides the same kind of feedback.

Examples of new products and techniques so developed in recent years are manifold. The most pervasive is the electronic computer. It is revolutionizing the management of large organizations, both in government and private industry, and is largely responsible for industrial automation. Under the missile and space programs, ever more complex computers are being developed. It is feasible right now to construct a master computer that might retain a complete record of all financial transactions in the United States, and thus keep watch on every citizen, making income-tax cheating virtually impossible. Whether such a step is desirable, however, is outside the scope of this book.

The feedback from space programs has come in new materials, low-temperature technology, medicine and chemistry, as well as electronics. Use of liquid oxygen on a large scale in rockets has developed that technology. As a result, liquid nitrogen, produced by the same method, is used to freeze whole blood for storage and as an agent for freezing food. Liquid oxygen itself provides a new and effective means of heating the fire in open-hearth furnaces to improve the quality of steel.

A drug derived from hydrazine, a rocket fuel, is used in treating mental illness. A ceramic material developed for missile radomes is good for kitchen utensils, since it can go from the deep freezer to the stove without cracking. Medical sensors devised to observe astronauts' reactions will prove useful in examining and treating earthbound patients.

Most future applications, however, cannot now be foreseen. Like all new developments, each use of technology developed for the space program must await the juncture of the need, the knowledge and the man with imagination and funds to introduce it. Some applications will come about promptly. Others may not emerge for many years. But in toto, use of the new knowledge will provide a continuing supply of new products, methods and industries, which will contribute to economic growth.

The moon program will not only provide new techniques. It will make fearsome demands of U.S. industry. Under the requirement of high-volume, low-cost production, standards of quality have suffered in recent years. Every so often, the U.S. automobile industry produces a "lemon." Household appliances break down with appalling regularity. Shoddy work has been responsible for missile failures. The stern reliability requirements involved in making equipment to operate in hostile space environments for months and perhaps years could bring about a return to an earlier tradition of fine craftsmanship. A by-product might be better, more durable goods for civilian use.

The moon expedition will make just as great demands on U.S. education. Scientists and engineers will be required in ever increasing numbers. To produce them, the nation will have to use all of its human resources. College education can no longer be restricted to that portion of the population able and willing to pay for it. Despite a rising trend of college costs, means will have to be found to enable qualified and ambitious students in the less privileged population groups—Negroes, Indians, Mexicans, Puerto Ricans, Orientals and so on—to attend college in just as great proportion as other elements of the population.

In graduate education, regional discrimination must be ended. Ways must be found to bring the numbers of postgraduate degrees awarded in the South, Southwest and Rocky Mountain regions up to the national average. More than half of the 9000 doctors of philosophy graduated in the nation annually are produced in the six states of Massachusetts, Indiana, New York, Illinois, California and Michigan. Students in education-poor states apparently do not go on to graduate study. National Science Foundation statistics show that fewer than one-eighth of all Ph.Ds attend universities more than 500 miles from their homes. Regional leaders must support such endeavors as Lloyd V. Berkner's Graduate Research Center at Dallas, the Association of Rocky Mountain Universities and Wernher von Braun's campaign for University of Alabama research facilities near the rocket center at Huntsville. Great national atomic energy laboratories, such as Brookhaven in New York, Argonne in Illinois and Lawrence Radiation in California, have encouraged the growth of nuclear physics in their regions. Southwesterners hope the establishment of the manned space flight center at Houston, Texas, will do as well for them in the space sciences.

Experience at the State University of Iowa, James A. Van Allen's institution, indicates that space research can generate great enthusiasm among science students. So far, only a few universities have contributed experiments for U.S. satellites. In the next few years, as larger satellites with room for many more experiments become available, Space Administrator James E. Webb hopes to persuade universities across the country to take part, and perhaps spark a nationwide upsurge of student interest in the physical sciences.

Participation is not limited to the United States. With the experience of the International Geophysical Year in mind, Congress in 1958 directed the government to cooperate with other nations and groups of nations in scientific space investigations and to develop peaceful applications of the results. In March, 1959, at a meeting of the international Committee on Space Research (COSPAR), NASA offered to place in orbit individual experiments or complete satellite payloads prepared by scientists of other nations.

The United Kingdom and Canada were the first to take up the proposition. Satellites designed for measurements of the ionosphere were due to be launched for both countries early in 1962. A second U.K. satellite is scheduled for 1963. Plans are also in preparation for launching French and Japanese satellites.

No money changes hands in the U.S. international space programs. If a foreign country is providing a satellite or a scientific experiment for a satellite, it pays the cost involved, while the United States pays the cost of whatever part of the job it has agreed to do. Besides the satellite ventures, NASA engages in cooperative projects to launch sounding rockets, perform ground-based research and exchange scientific personnel. Each project is judged on the basis of whether it contributes to the U.S. scientific program; that is, the experiment must meet the same standards that it would if proposed by an American scientist.

Up to 1961, about fifteen countries had sent scientists to U.S. laboratories on lengthy visits to familiarize themselves with space techniques. Most are surprised to learn that the NASA centers are wide open; there are few secrets. NASA policy, under the mandate of the 1958 law, is to conduct space science programs openly and to share techniques and results with scientists the world over. The motive is not simply altruism. U.S. scientists believe that a free flow of information will advance scientific progress and increase the world's total of brainpower applied to space problems. A discovery in a laboratory in Japan or Brazil may make possible a spectacular American achievement. By developing cooperative arrangements with scientists around the world, NASA is in effect putting them to work to help American astronauts win the race for the moon. Russia, which surrounds its space program with deep secrecy, has access only to the writings of foreign scientists and to what it can learn at the major international meetings.

The value of the American policy far exceeds the scientific benefits, however. Although only two nations have the capacity to launch satellites, space exploration has captured the imagination of the world. By bringing other countries into its program, the United States makes them partners in the endeavor and thus improves its relationships with allies and neutrals during the protracted East-West struggle.

Space programs in cooperation with allies are good for allied morale. Cooperation with neutrals influences them on behalf of the United States and the things America stands for. When Vice President Lyndon Johnson visited India in 1961, he stayed up half the night with Prime Minister Nehru, he reported, "talking about how we could explore space together."

Last, but not least of the benefits of the race for the moon, is the effect on American morale. The adventure creates a national feeling of unity. The day after President Kennedy announced the program, Secretary of Labor Arthur J. Goldberg was able to announce a labor-management truce at missile- and space-launching bases. In its first few months, the number of man-hours lost through strikes and lockouts was less than five per cent of the figure beforehand. William E. Simkin, director of the Federal Mediation and Conciliation Service, said there was no doubt that the moon program helped bring about the truce.

Across America, half the population of the country held its collective breath to watch on television and listen by radio as Alan Shepard flew into space on the morning of May 5, 1961. He was figuratively lifted by a mass outpouring of national will. The experience of sharing future, more ambitious ventures will create a national sense of common purpose that cannot be attained otherwise except in time of war.

IV TO THE MOON

15. DECISION

SPACE IS OUR GREAT NEW FRONTIER," Senator John F. Kennedy declared in the 1960 presidential campaign. He promised to assign responsibility for the program to dedicated men, who would have "a mandate to speed the decision-making process, and authority to make affirmative decisions very quickly."

Kennedy made his own first decision on space a few weeks after the election. After a visit to Lyndon B. Johnson's Texas ranch, the President-elect announced he had asked Johnson to head the National Aeronautics and Space Council, a top-level body established by law to advise the President, chaired by the President, of which President Eisenhower had made little use. Kennedy also gave Johnson an assignment to recommend a man to head the space administration.

Johnson's search for an executive brought into the open a three-way tug-of-war. Advocates of a strong civilian space program faced opposition on the one hand from influential scientists who wanted to curtail manned space exploration and on the other from the military-industrial complex. The latter group sought to turn the space program over to the Air Force. As a result, several prominent businessmen and scientists who were approached were not interested. They had no desire to take over an agency to preside over its dissolution.

The lukewarm or negative attitude of many leading scientists about exploring space convinced Johnson that he did not want to recommend one to head the agency. Indeed, some of those

[189

suggested for the post by the scientific community were men who had made public statements in opposition to manned space flight. Inasmuch as other factors than science were involved in the space program, Johnson and his advisers sought a man who would administer and set policy from a broad national viewpoint, and not limit the program to basic scientific research. Administrative experience was clearly desirable for a man who would run so large an operation. Even then, NASA had a budget of more than a billion dollars a year. But men with ability and broad national outlook were rare. By January 20, 1961, the day the Kennedy administration took office, Johnson still had found no space administrator. Five days later, in an obvious move to put pressure on the Vice President, Kennedy told his press conference that an appointment would be made by the end of that week.

Johnson asked some Congressional leaders for suggestions. Senator Robert S. Kerr, who had succeeded the Vice President as chairman of the Senate Space Committee, put forward a name that met all of the criteria, a businessman and lawyer who had served in high government posts, run large organizations and, through public-service activities on behalf of education and science, was known to many scientific leaders. Kerr's nominee was James E. Webb, who had been associated with the senator for eight years in the management of the Kerr-McGee Oil Company.

Webb had served six years in the Truman administration, including three as Director of the Bureau of the Budget and three as Under Secretary of State. In business, he had risen from personnel manager to vice president of the Sperry Gyroscope Company between 1936 and 1943; and from 1953 to 1958 was chief executive officer of the Republic Supply Company, a Kerr-McGee subsidiary that manufactured oil-field equipment. Kerr, understandably partial, says Webb has "the greatest mental energy and capacity for sustained mental and physical effort of anyone I know," and adds that Webb has "probably the broadest knowledge of the operation of the Executive Branch of our government of anyone appointed by President Kennedy to any position." A former Marine aviator, Webb was familiar with the aircraft industry from the period in the 1930s when he was a clerk in the Washington law firm of O. Max Gardner, former governor of North Carolina who was general counsel of the Aeronautical

Chamber of Commerce. After leaving the government in 1952, Webb became a director of the McDonnell Aircraft Company of St. Louis.

Born in North Carolina in 1906, Webb was the second of five children and the eldest son of John Frederick Webb, school superintendent of Granville County, in the north-central part of the state. He acquired a lifelong taste for being at the center of large affairs in 1932-34 as administrative assistant to Congressman Edward W. Pou of North Carolina, chairman of the House Rules Committee. He has developed a specialty of getting large organizations to run smoothly and avoid administrative conflict. As budget director, he made the bureau an institution of the government, rather than a creature of the President, by establishing formal liaison with the Congressional leaders when the Republicans took power after the 1946 elections. As Under Secretary of State, he gave his major attention to internal administration and relations with Congress and the other executive departments.

While in Oklahoma, Webb often told associates he preferred to devote two-thirds of his time to public service and only a third to earning a living. First, however, he had to become financially independent. He felt he had earned enough after five years at the head of Republic Supply and resigned in 1959 from full-time activity with the oil business. He stayed on only as a part-time director and assistant to the president of Kerr-McGee Industries.

Returning to Washington, Webb spent most of his time on three major non-profit enterprises, the Municipal Manpower Commission, Educational Services Incorporated and the Meridian House Foundation. The Ford Foundation had established the manpower commission with a half-million-dollar grant to study the needs of urban government in the United States for trained personnel. Educational Services Incorporated, which had evolved from an organization begun by physicists at Massachusetts Institute of Technology to set up a new high-school course in physics, needed strong leadership to solve administrative problems involved in such activities as publishing paper-back books. Meridian House Foundation operates the Washington International Center, an orientation center for government-sponsored foreign visitors.

Thus, although not a scientist himself, Webb was known to

scientists through the publishing venture. They also knew him as a trustee and first president of Frontiers of Science Foundation of Oklahoma, a former director of the Oak Ridge Institute of Nuclear Studies, a former member of the National Advisory Cancer Council of the Public Health Service and a member of a panel of consultants on medical research and education to the secretary of health, education and welfare. He was a long-time friend of Lloyd V. Berkner, chairman of the Space Science Board, having served with him in the Marine Corps. He was also a friend of Jerome B. Wiesner, the President's science adviser, having worked with him in science and education activities.

When Kennedy approved the selection, it was Wiesner who telephoned Webb in Oklahoma City on January 27 to offer him the post. Webb pointed out both to Wiesner and, later, to Kennedy, that he had no experience in science and engineering. Kennedy replied that he wanted an administrator with experience in policy formulation. Nevertheless, when Kennedy announced the appointment on January 30, there was a bitter reaction from scientists, both inside and outside of the space agency. "The scientific side of NASA has let it be known in a multitude of loud voices," reported *Aviation Daily,* a trade publication, "that they don't like the Webb appointment. What the technical people wanted was a scientist to head the agency. . . ."

The scientists' objection to Webb was not an abstract question of principle. They wanted scientists to set policy. The conservative leadership of the scientific community was in violent disagreement with continuing manned exploration of space. Scientists outside the agency and some within wanted to prevent any further man-in-space program beyond Project Mercury, just then being studied, or at least to hold it to a low level of funding and priority. Under instructions from departing Administrator Glennan, Abraham Hyatt, Director of Program Planning and Evaluation, was at the head of a group studying three alternative long-range plans—one directed at further scientific exploration of the moon and planets, with unmanned vehicles; one directed at applications such as communications and weather observation, and one directed at a manned landing on the moon. A group headed by George M. Low, Director of Manned Space Flight, was studying details of the problems involved in the manned lunar landing.

Some of the nation's most eminent scientists threw their influence against any such project. Vannevar Bush, who had headed the Office of Scientific Research and Development during World War II, told a Congressional committee that exploring space would be cheaper with instruments and "man can do no more than an instrument, probably less." James R. Killian, who had served as President Eisenhower's first scientific adviser, had long opposed what he called letting the Soviets set American scientific policy, by forcing America to imitate them. George B. Kistiakowski, who succeeded Killian, declared that man in space was a "scientific luxury that should not be allowed to divert national efforts from more urgent scientific challenges here on earth."

Such intellectual leaders as historian Arnold Toynbee declared that a race into space between the United States and Russia was "a rather childish competition. We should use the resources for something quite different, for raising the standard of living for the great mass of the human race here on earth."

This was not the first time, however, that Webb had become embroiled in controversy with the leaders of American science. From 1946 to 1949, as budget director, he had been a close adviser to President Truman during the negotiations that led up to the establishment of the National Science Foundation. Leaders of the scientific community wanted the foundation to be independent, responsive to them rather than the President. Finding sympathetic ears in the Republican leadership of the Eightieth Congress, they obtained passage of a bill that established a twenty-four-member board of scientists, appointed by the President to overlapping six-year terms. The board would have had independent power to appoint a director.

Webb, however, insisted that scientific decisions have too profound an effect on the nation and the world to be left entirely to scientists—that giving the board independent power would establish a scientific oligarchy that would be a law unto itself. Truman, on Webb's advice, vetoed the bill on August 6, 1947. Webb wrote the veto message, which declared it tended to insulate the foundation director from presidential authority. After a three-year dispute, Truman and Webb won a clear victory. Congress passed a measure under which a foundation director would also be appointed by the President for a six-year term. Truman approved it May 10, 1950.

In 1961, Webb disregarded the scientists' protests and plunged into work. Within the first two weeks after he took office February 14, he had set in motion a re-examination of the ten-year space program and the funding necessary to carry it out. On February 24, he learned that preponderant scientific opinion within the space agency favored manned space exploration. Associate Administrator Robert C. Seamans Jr. laid a staff-recommended program of priorities before Webb and his deputy, Hugh L. Dryden, whom Kennedy had reappointed from the Eisenhower administration. The program called for larger rockets, development of man-in-space technology and exploration of the moon.

Three days later, the new administrator found that the outside scientific world was not unanimous in its opposition. Lloyd V. Berkner, chairman of the Space Science Board, told Webb that body favored a program leading to manned exploration of the moon and the planets, in which scientists as well as pilot astronauts would take part. Berkner also urged the construction of new rockets, much larger than those designed for military purposes.

Thus fortified with scientific support, Webb felt free to exercise his own judgment on the basis of nonscientific questions of public policy. After four weeks in office, he endorsed an acceleration of the space program under which a landing on the moon might be accomplished by the 1969-70 period, instead of "after 1970" as had been provided by the previous administration. To carry out the acceleration, he asked the Budget Bureau for an addition of $308 million to the Eisenhower space budget of $1.1 billion for the coming year. He committed himself publicly to advancing the technology of manned space flight on March 17, in a speech before the American Astronautical Society. Webb announced that he was reviewing the rate at which progress could be made toward the "next intermediate goal of manned space flight, that is the manned space station."

But the Budget Bureau, under instruction from Kennedy to seek to balance the nonmilitary portion of the budget, proposed that only $50 million of the $308 million be approved. The final decision, however, was up to the President. On the evening of March 20, Webb passed up a Presbyterian dinner at a church in neighboring Alexandria, Virginia, to work late at his office preparing a long memorandum for Kennedy. In it, he pointed out the national issues involved, and recounted how Eisenhower's skepticism had prevented adequate funding in the past.

By this time, Kennedy felt the time was ripe to make a public move. In the first two months of his administration, Kennedy had directed his attention almost wholly to domestic affairs. The 1960-61 recession was causing national concern and White House advisers felt that action on a subject so remote from bread-and-butter problems would be politically unsound at the very beginning of a new administration. But by March 22, he had completed his preliminary actions on the domestic scene and so, on the recommendation of the Vice President, Wiesner, Webb, General Schriever and Deputy Defense Secretary Roswell Gilpatric, Kennedy sent to the Senate the nomination of Edward C. Welsh, a legislative assistant to Senator Stuart Symington of Missouri, as executive secretary of the National Aeronautics and Space Council.

The nomination filled a post that had been vacant since it was created by the Space Act of 1958. Creation of the council had been written into the act at Johnson's urging when he was chairman of a special Senate committee on space. He saw it as a means of solving interagency disputes, particularly between the new space agency and the military services. One of the jobs of the council staff specified in the law was to prepare recommendations on such disputes from an impartial viewpoint.

Eisenhower had preferred to deal with space matters mostly through his scientific advisers, viewing the space program as just another form of scientific research. Thus the scientific view prevailed with him on the question of manned space flight. In his final budget message of January, 1961, Eisenhower said, "Further testing and experimentation will be necessary to establish whether there are any valid scientfiic reasons for extending manned space flight beyond the Mercury program."

By deciding to employ the Space Council as his means of dealing with the program, Kennedy institutionalized the fact that other considerations than science are involved in the formation of presidential space policy. However, no administrator of a federal agency can be happy about the interposition of a new office between him and the President. Both Glennan and Webb maintained that they could solve any difficulties with the Defense Department by direct negotiation. But the space administrator must deal with the defense secretary or his deputy. The

Space Council executive secretary can deal with them and also reach down into Defense and other departments and agencies to do business directly with the people involved in space programs, and can sometimes approach closer to the heart of a controversy.

Like Webb, Welsh is no scientist, unless a doctorate in economics can qualify him for that title. After twelve years on university faculties, Welsh joined the government in 1942 as an executive in the Office of Price Administration, becoming deputy administrator in 1946. During 1947-50, he was on General Douglas MacArthur's staff in the occupation of Japan, responsible for the reorganization of the Japanese economy and the dissolution of cartels. He had become associated with Symington in 1950 when the latter was chairman of the National Security Resources Board, and had gone on with him to the Reconstruction Finance Corporation in 1951. On various occasions, he was acting head of those two agencies. He again joined Symington in the Senate in 1953.

Kennedy turned his attention to space on March 22, the day he sent the Welsh nomination to the Senate. On the same day, he received the Webb memorandum and called for a briefing on the space program at a late afternoon meeting. Among those present were Johnson, Webb, Wiesner, Welsh, Dryden and Budget Director David Bell. The briefing took more than two hours; Kennedy made no decision then. The next day, he called Johnson, Wiesner, Bell and Welsh back for discussions. Johnson and Welsh supported NASA strongly and emphasized the urgency of getting a big rocket program started quickly. Wiesner, although dubious at first, also supported an increase. Bell, having expressed his view on budget balancing, indicated he would do everything he could to carry out whatever decision the President made.

Kennedy favored an increase. The last thing he wanted to do, however, was to commit himself to a major revision of policy without getting the facts on the over-all space requirements as well as some idea of the public receptivity. As a result, Kennedy committed himself to the faster program for boosters, but held off on the complete funding until he had more facts. Nevertheless, the implication of his decision was approval of the Apollo manned spacecraft, since there was no other important proposed use of the big rockets. The budget revision submitted to Congress March 28 called for an addition of $125.67 million to begin work on a bigger Saturn, the C-2, and to speed work on still larger liquid-fueled rockets and the nuclear rocket.

Meanwhile, the Senate confirmed Welsh promptly and his first assignment was to draft amendments to the Space Act that would take the President off the Space Council, out of a position in which he had the job of advising himself. As a result, a presidential message was sent to Congress April 10. The bill, establishing the Vice President as chairman, was enacted April 25.

Russia's Yuri Gagarin made his orbital flight on April 12, while the Kennedy budget revisions were before the House Space Committee. It was the first Soviet space spectacular ever launched at quite so fortuitous a time for the U.S. space budget. Observers could not help joking that the Kennedy administration must have planned it.

Congressional reaction was easy to predict. The House Space Committee called Webb and Dryden to a special hearing the following day. Chairman Overton Brooks asked Webb whether NASA's long range plan called for "catching up with the Russians." The administrator could make no such promise. He replied that Kennedy had made the fundamental decision to go ahead with rockets needed to carry vehicles like Apollo into space, but not at maximum pace, adding: "Certainly you can proceed faster than the funds recommended by President Kennedy."

If Congress should wish to add further funds, Webb said, "I will take every step necessary to carry out the decision that is made and to do everything possible to realize the maximum rate of progress from the resources provided." The decision before the nation, he continued, is "whether we now expect to proceed as we did in connection with the atomic bomb, with a substantial number of efforts going on in parallel, with all of the resources that may be required to do this."

James G. Fulton, a Pennsylvania Republican, asked a key question: How much could the lunar landing be accelerated and what would it cost? Webb declined to estimate the possible acceleration on the basis of his limited experience. As to the cost, he replied, "There are very large numbers that people use. Some people use a number as high as $40 billion to land a man on the moon. Others say half that amount."

The next day, the senior member of the permanent staff of

NASA was on the committee's witness stand. Associate Administrator Robert C. Seamans Jr. was thoroughly familiar with the studies conducted by the Hyatt and Low committees. This time, the question was asked by David S. King, a Utah Democrat.

"I understand," King began, "the Russians have indicated at various times that their goal is to get a man on the moon and return safely by 1967, the fiftieth anniversary of the Bolshevik Revolution. Now specifically I would like to know, yes or no, are we making that specific target date to try to equal or surpass their achievement?"

Seamans repeated that the target date was 1969 or 1970. "That outlines the issue very squarely. As things are now programmed we have lost," King continued. "Do you think it would be conceivably possible by increasing appropriations, by marshaling our manpower and resources and everything else that we have available, to meet this target date of, let us say, 1967?"

"This is really a very major undertaking," Seamans replied. "To compress the program by three years means that greatly increased funding would be required for the interval between now and 1967. I certainly cannot state that this is an impossible objective. If it comes down to a matter of national policy, I would be the first to review it wholeheartedly and see what it would take to do the job. My estimate at this moment is that the goal may very well be achievable."

Seamans said the rate of expenditure would probably reach a level of $4 to $5 billion a year if such a schedule were established. A conservative voice soon made itself heard. J. Edgar Chenoweth, Colorado Republican, commented: "Do you agree we face a rather serious national decision here? I think it is not for this committee to make, but to be decided at a much higher level, whether or not it is in the best interests of this country, whether our economy can stand perhaps double or treble the present funding or even go higher than that, by putting up money to achieve this lunar shot, say in 1967 or even before."

"I think it is a decision to be made by the people of the United States," Seamans replied.

"I disagree," Chenoweth said. "The people of this country do not have the technical knowledge on this subject that you have. When you talk about putting a man on the moon, they don't know what you are talking about. They don't know what expenditure is involved, nor the scientific and research work that has to be done. We can't expect them to make that decision."

"Is this not our responsibility as representatives of the people?" asked George P. Miller, California Democrat.

"We can make the decision," Chenoweth responded. "But I think when it comes to affecting the economy and the fiscal policies of this country and the tremendous amounts of money that are involved, I think perhaps this will have to be made at a higher level of the administration."

Six days later, the question reached the highest level. On April 20, Kennedy directed Vice President Johnson to investigate what could be done. In a five-paragraph memorandum, Kennedy asked:

—Where do we stand in space? Can we beat the Soviets?

—What can we do about going to the moon? Is there any other space program that promises dramatic results, in which we could win?

—Are we working twenty-four hours a day? If not, why not?

—What about rocket boosters? Which should we emphasize, nuclear, solid or liquid fuels or a combination of the three?

—Are we making maximum effort? Are we achieving the necessary results? *

Johnson used the machinery of the Space Council to conduct the overall study. Aided by Welsh, he began holding meetings with NASA, the Defense Department, the Atomic Energy Commission and Wiesner's office. In an innovation suggested by Welsh, representatives of the Bureau of the Budget attended too, so that the bureau would be fully aware of the large sums of money that would be needed. The Vice President also set up special purpose panels.

On April 24, he called on three outstanding businessmen for advice. Frank Stanton, president of the Columbia Broadcasting System, George R. Brown, a Houston, Texas oil and gas man, and Donald C. Cook, executive vice president for the American Electric Power Service Corporation of New York, met with Johnson, Wiesner, Webb, Dryden, Welsh and Wernher von Braun. On another occasion, Johnson met with a panel consisting of von Braun, General Schriever and Vice Admiral John T. Hayward. Meanwhile, Wiesner was meeting with scientific panels and feeding the results to Welsh. In Congress, Johnson and

* The questions are paraphrased. I have not actually seen the memorandum.

Welsh consulted the chairmen of the space committees, Senator Robert S. Kerr of Oklahoma and the late Representative Overton Brooks of Louisiana.

Johnson also asked the ranking Republicans on the space committees—Senator Styles Bridges of New Hampshire and Congressman Fulton of Pennsylvania—whether they could generate support for a vastly increased program on their side of the aisle. Both said they would. All of the consultants were asked to submit their views in writing.

The Stanton-Brown-Cook panel of businessmen, at a second meeting on May 3, with Johnson, Webb, Welsh, Dryden and Senators Kerr and Bridges, agreed that there were strong national policy reasons for conducting a vigorous program. "The goal that we must set is the achievement of leadership in space," Cook wrote in a later memorandum, "leadership which is both clear-cut and acknowledged. Our objective must be, therefore, not merely to overtake, but substantially to outdistance Russia. Any program with a lesser basic objective would be a second-rate program, worthy only of a second-class power. And, most important, a lesser program would raise serious questions among other countries as to whether, as a nation, we had the will and the discipline necessary for leadership in the struggle to preserve a free society."

The von Braun-Schriever-Hayward panel agreed that the program was feasible technically and well within the capacity of the American economy. "There are three questions," Schriever said later. "Is it important that we compete with Russia? My unequivocal view is yes, it is overridingly important. Second, do we have a chance if we do compete. Unequivocally yes. We are still way ahead of Russia in total capacity. Question three, can we afford it? I'm not an economist but nobody can tell me we can't afford it. Anyone who says we don't have the capacity is a defeatist. We need more of the attitude of Roosevelt, who said he wanted 50,000 planes a year—and got them."

"It is certainly feasible," Hayward also told me. "Like everything else, it is a function of the effort put in. Many things will have to be done, but there is no technical reason why we can't. Suppose we have to launch from the poles, to avoid the radiation belts. It would be much harder and more expensive, but we could do it."

Johnson's discussions with Congressional leaders assured him there would be little trouble there. However, he had a bit of difficulty getting together with Chairman Brooks of the House committee for a discussion. The first date had to be canceled because of a House debate on the minimum wage bill and the second because of a meeting of the National Security Council. However, Johnson asked Brooks for a memorandum on the nation's space needs as he saw them.

The House committee chairman urged a full-steam program to fly communications, weather, navigation and astronomical observatory satellites as soon as possible, so as to gain "first" over Russia soon. He also favored a program for a lunar landing, but he did not feel ready to say that the people would support the large expenditures that would be needed to carry that program at a maximum rate. He feared that the funds might have to be diverted from defense.

One further event was to serve as a test of the political water temperature. On May 5, Alan B. Shepard Jr. made the first suborbital flight in Project Mercury. Its success, and the enthusiastic reaction at home and abroad, provided convincing evidence that a big space program would receive support. On Saturday, May 6, the day after the shot, Webb met with Secretary of Defense Robert S. McNamara at the Pentagon to work out the final version of the plan, which had been developed as a result of the meetings and memoranda prepared under Space Council auspices, Webb and McNamara's deputy, Roswell Gilpatric, spent the weekend putting it together. The plan went to Johnson as a joint Webb-McNamara recommendation on May 8, the same day that Shepard and his fellow astronauts were in Washington for a round of public appearances and a White House ceremony at which Kennedy awarded Shepard the space agency's distinguished service medal.

Johnson carried the recommendations to the President on the same day with the report that a few loose ends of coordination still had to be tied down. The major feature of the moon program was a decision to carry on parallel development of two separate rocket boosters, one with liquid fuels and one with solid fuels, under a project called Nova. The space agency would be in charge of establishing over-all requirements and the development of the liquid-fueled rocket. The Air Force would develop the solid-fueled rocket to meet the space agency requirements.

By 1964 or thereabouts, NASA would decide which rocket system was to be used for the moon expedition.

The program included three other elements not directly related to the moon expedition. One was acceleration of the development of the nuclear rocket, Project Rover, with the aim of a flight test by 1966. When the moon flight was targeted for about 1970, the nuclear rocket was considered one of the major candidates for providing the propulsion. But everyone agreed that it would be impossible for a nuclear rocket to meet the 1967 manned flight date. In the new program the nuclear rocket was directed toward use as a secondary method of accomplishing the lunar flight and, in the period after 1970, for manned exploration of the planets. Large increases in funds were also included for the weather and communication satellite programs, so that they could move as rapidly as possible toward operational status.

The plan called for increases, over and above Kennedy's March recommendations, totaling $702 million for the coming fiscal year. Most of the money, $549 million, would go to the space agency, with the rest divided among the Defense Department, the Weather Bureau and the Atomic Energy Commission. The increase would bring the government's total authority to commit funds for space projects to a level just over $3 billion for the fiscal year ending June 30, 1962. The schedule called for the aggregate total to reach about $28 billion for the five years ending June 30, 1966.

While the new program was being given final polish, Kennedy sent Johnson on an eleven-day good-will tour of the Far East. During the Vice President's absence, the President held one final meeting of advisers to determine strategy for presenting the program to Congress. The decision was to hold it up and submit it together with several unrelated items in a package as a second State of the Union address. The White House staff felt that if he kept sending a series of money requests to Congress, the total would appear to be more than if all were sent at once.

The President delivered the message in person on May 25, the day after Johnson's return. It included proposals on a wide variety of subjects—Communist activities among the uncommitted nations, economic and social progress in the United States and abroad, worldwide information activities, defense alliances, military and intelligence organization, civil defense and disarmament.

"Finally," Kennedy declared, "if we are to win the battle for men's minds, the dramatic achievements in space which occurred in recent weeks should have made clear to us all the impact of this new frontier of human adventure. Since early in my term, our efforts in space have been under review. With the advice of the Vice President we have examined where we are strong and where we are not, where we may succeed and where we may not. Now it is time to take longer strides—time for a great new American enterprise—time for this nation to take a clearly leading role in space achievement.

"I believe we possess all the resources and all the talents necessary. But the facts of the matter are that we have never made the national decisions or marshaled the national resources required for such leadership. We have never specified long-range goals on an urgent time schedule, or managed our resources and our time so as to insure their fulfillment.

"Recognizing the head start obtained by the Soviets with their large rocket engines, which gives them many months of lead-time, and recognizing the likelihood that they will exploit this lead for some time to come in still more impressive successes, we nevertheless are required to make new efforts. For while we cannot guarantee that we shall one day be first, we can guarantee that any failure to share this effort will make us last. We take an additional risk by making it in full view of the world—but as shown by the feat of astronaut Shepard, this very risk enhances our stature when we are successful. But this is not merely a race. Space is open to us now; and our eagerness to share its meaning is not governed by the efforts of others. We go into space because whatever mankind must undertake, *free* men must fully share. . . .

"I believe that this nation should commit itself to achieving the goal, before this decade is out, of landing a man on the moon and returning him safely to earth. No single space project in this period will be more exciting, or more impressive, or more important for the long-range exploration of space; and none will be so difficult or expensive to accomplish. . . . In a very real sense, it will not be just one man going to the moon—it will be an entire nation. For all of us must work to put him there. . . .

"Let it be clear," the President continued, "that I am asking Congress and the country to accept a firm commitment to a new course of action—a course which will last for many years and carry very heavy costs—an estimated $7-$9 billion additional over the next five years. If we were to go only half way, or reduce our sights in the face of difficulty, it would be better not to go at all.

"Let me stress also that more money alone will not do the job. This decision demands a major national commitment of scientific and technical manpower, material and facilities, and the possibility of their diversion from other important activities where they are thinly spread. It means a degree of dedication, organization and discipline which have not always characterized our research and development efforts. It means we cannot afford undue work stoppages, inflated costs of material or talent, wasteful interagency rivalries, or a high turnover of key personnel.

"New objectives and new money cannot solve these problems. They could, in fact, aggravate them further—unless every scientist, every engineer, every serviceman, every technician, contractor, and civil servant involved gives his personal pledge that this nation will move forward, with the full speed of freedom, in the exciting adventure of space."

Despite the magnitude of the decision before Congress and a complex series of legislative hurdles, there was little debate. Congress, in the three and a half years since Sputnik, had talked itself out and was impatient to act. Further, the President's declaration had put the nation's prestige at stake. Congressman Fulton likened the situation to that of June, 1950, when President Truman sent American troops to Korea, then came back to Congress for funds. "Once the President says it's a race," Fulton asked, "how can you vote against it?" Washington correspondents called the space race "the legislative equivalent of war."

Space budgets must go through Congress twice—first in an authorization bill and then as an appropriation. The Kennedy message arrived just a day after the House had passed an authorization bill based on his previous recommendations, and the House Appropriations Committee had already reported out its catch-all appropriation for independent agencies, in which both NASA and Space Council funds are included.

The Senate took up the House authorization bill June 28

and amended it to provide the full $1.784 billion Kennedy had sought in his final request. The action was unanimous, without even the formality of a roll call. Then the measure went to a conference committee and the House conferees agreed to the Senate amendments. The House approved the conference report on July 20 by a vote of 354 to 59. Brooks supported the bill in the debate.

On the appropriation itself, the House passed a first-round measure on June 7 that was $35 million less than Kennedy had requested on his first round in March. That bill went to the Senate, which on July 31 amended it to provide $1.749 billion, a reduction of the same $35 million from Kennedy's final request. A conference committee on August 4 agreed on a compromise total of $1,671,750,000. That bill passed both houses on August 7.

Congress thus voted $113 million less for the space agency than Kennedy had requested. However, it had become an annual custom for NASA to return to Congress in January for additional funds. There was a general assumption on Capitol Hill that the agency would do so again in January, 1962, if necessary.

Thus the United States, in less than seven months after the new administration took office, committed itself to the most ambitious peaceful enterprise in the history of mankind. Timetables were established, but no one really knew how long it would take before the first American set foot on the moon. Cost estimates were made, but no one could truly predict the cost. Every reasonable precaution was to be taken, but no one could promise that lives would not be lost.

The nation was committed, not to a whirlwind effort promising quick victory, but to a campaign requiring steady effort over many years. There was one overriding question. Were the American people capable of such dedication?

16. ORGANIZING THE VENTURE

HEN PRESIDENT KENNEDY assigned the lunar landing mission to the National Aeronautics and Space Administration, the agency was not organized to manage a job of such great size and urgency. A jerry-built structure slapped together hastily in 1958, NASA had been growing rapidly and without pause up to the time of the 1961 decision. Organizational weakness was apparent even to outsiders. In January, 1961, before the Kennedy administration took office, an ad hoc committee headed by Jerome Wiesner recommended to the President-elect that NASA be reorganized to establish more effective management.

The space administration was built around the National Advisory Committee for Aeronautics, an organization of very competent scientists and engineers who conducted aeronautical and rocket research at five stations across the country, four laboratories and a launching base on the eastern shore of Virginia. On formation in October, 1958, the 8000 people of NACA and 200 from the Naval Research Laboratory's Project Vanguard were combined. A month later, NASA assumed direction of a staff of 2400 at the Jet Propulsion Laboratory, operated by contract at the California Institute of Technology. By hiring steadily in its first twenty-one months of existence, the space agency built its staff, exclusive of the Jet Propulsion Laboratory, to a little over 10,000.

On July 1, 1960, NASA took over Wernher von Braun's rocket-building group, consisting of 4500 persons, at the Army Ballistic

Missile Agency in Huntsville, Alabama, and reconstituted it the George C. Marshall Space Flight Center. The Marshall Center also grew steadily.

Meanwhile, the space agency established two entirely new field organizations. At Langley Field, Virginia, using the facilities of the old NACA Langley Research Center, a Space Task Group was set up to run Project Mercury. And at Greenbelt, Maryland, fifteen miles northeast of Washington, NASA built the Goddard Space Flight Center to operate its unmanned satellite, sounding rocket and space science programs. By July 1, 1961, the space administration staff had grown to almost 16,500 and an increase of another 3000 was indicated for the next twelve months. The responsible top people came from varying backgrounds, but almost all had one thing in common. They had come to their positions from field installations rather than national headquarters. Very few knew their way around Washington bureaucracy.

The NACA had never been responsible itself for monitoring large industrial contracts although it had worked closely with the Air Force on aircraft development. The new organization adopted Air Force methods and procedures for dealing with industry. The Vanguard group brought with them the habit of using Navy methods. The von Braun group came in with the Army approach plus a background of experience under different conditions in Germany.

The Air Force tends to give industry a free hand. The Army generally follows the "arsenal concept," which involves production or close supervision of production by government employees at a government arsenal. The Navy varies from bureau to bureau between the two points of view. The differing philosophies within the space agency sometimes led to lengthy disputes. In addition, the former NACA scientists and engineers tended on occasion to take a perfectionist attitude about technical details. The conflicting philosophies of management and the tendency to perfectionism led to delays, which in turn led critics in industry to charge NASA officials with lacking a sense of urgency.

The space agency's reputation in industry was also damaged by its obedience to the policies of the Eisenhower administration. In January, 1960, the technical staff laid before Administrator Glennan a proposal for a three-man spacecraft to follow

Project Mercury. Glennan, aware of the President's skeptical attitude toward man in space, would support only studies of the project—not a penny for building hardware. To avoid appearing to disagree with the President, scientists of the agency adopted the party line that more study was needed to determine the effect of radiation and weightlessness on humans. This was true, of course. But it was equally true that, if the project had been considered urgent, the hardware could have been built earlier than has been done in Project Apollo.

The careful NASA adherence to the party line was contrasted with the attitude of the military services, which did not accept Eisenhower's word as final when he put thumbs down on a project. If the service involved considered it urgent, industrial contractors were encouraged to bring the word to Congress. Then a committee might call before it the responsible officer, who would admit under questioning that he needed more money. Often such a procedure succeeded in getting funds appropriated, whereupon Eisenhower would relent and allow them to be used. This was such a common practice that the refusal of NASA officials to take similar action was interpreted as a lack of enthusiasm for their program.

Organizationally, the great weakness of NASA was in its top staff. The agency was headed by a triumvirate—administrator, deputy administrator and associate administrator—who had to depend on the heads of NASA technical offices for all of their information. As a result, major decisions were made in the technical offices without reference to general management; real problems were not brought to general management until they were "solved." The field centers reported to the all-powerful technical offices.

At first, there were two technical offices—one supervising the former NACA research centers and one supervising the space programs. When the von Braun rocket group joined NASA, a third technical office was established, to manage rocket programs. Later, a fourth office was established to supervise life science programs.

By separating the rockets and the space payloads into separate technical offices, the space agency violated a primary principle of modern management, the so-called systems concept. The concept is a rather elementary notion that one manager should be in charge of any one job—that the whole job should be considered in toto, as a system. By drawing an arbitrary line between the payload and the final rocket stage, NASA created two managers for every job it had to do. In fact, the principle of the division was not always carried out in practice. When trouble developed with the Atlas launching rocket for Project Mercury in 1960 and 1961, Abe Silverstein, director of Space Flight Programs, worked out a solution despite the fact that his office was responsible only for payloads. Nevertheless, the division hampered work.

The creation of an Office of Life Science Programs added further to the confusion. Some life science work was directly related to Project Mercury. Some involved basic science, such as the search for life on the moon and other planets. Some involved advancing the state of technology—for instance, improving life support systems for manned spacecraft. There was no focus to the work the office supervised. As a result, its establishment inspired concern in the military services, all of which had extensive life science programs, that NASA would attempt to take them over.

The Wiesner committee recommended that NASA be reorganized so that technical offices would be oriented toward the tasks to be accomplished rather than the type of technology to be utilized. It recommended offices for four major areas—propulsion and vehicle design and development, the space sciences, nonmilitary exploitation of space technology, and aeronautical sciences and aircraft development. In choosing an administrator, Kennedy had problems of organization at the top of his list. Thus it is not surprising that he selected Webb, a specialist in managing large enterprises.

The two other members of the ruling triumvirate of the space agency were unchanged by the new administration. Kennedy reappointed the deputy administrator, Hugh L. Dryden, who had headed the old NACA for eleven years before it was incorporated into NASA. The associate administrator, Robert C. Seamans Jr., was not a presidential appointee.

Dryden, born in 1898 at Pocomoke City, Maryland, and educated at Johns Hopkins University, was a scientist who had served with the National Bureau of Standards from 1920 to 1947, rising to associate director before he was chosen to head the NACA. He has published many technical reports in his specialty of aerodynamics and is the holder of many scientific honors.

Seamans, the youngest of the top three, joined the space agency less than five months before the change of administration. He is a Massachusetts native, born in 1918, who attended Harvard with President Kennedy (and knew him casually), then went on to graduate studies at Massachusetts Institute of Technology. His New Frontier credentials would be perfect except that he is a Republican. Seamans taught and conducted electronic research and development at MIT from 1941 to 1955, when he became manager of the Airborne Systems Laboratory of the Radio Corporation of America.

Following the decision to undertake the lunar landing project, Webb considered bringing in some well-known executive as "czar" of the enterprise. But after four months of deliberation, he decided to give day-to-day charge to Seamans. The reorganization left Webb and Dryden free for major policy decisions and long-range planning. Seamans' major initial task was to recruit outstanding managerial talent from industry.

The reorganization, announced in September, 1961, wiped the organizational chart clean, created four new technical offices and gave Seamans a deputy to aid him in managing the vast program that would develop. The deputy is Thomas F. Dixon, former vice president of the Rocketdyne Division of North American Aviation, who had been involved in rocket development work for fourteen years and had directed the most successful American liquid-propellant rockets. Dixon was born in 1916 in Nashville, Tennessee, and attended Vanderbilt University and the University of Michigan. Seamans will concentrate on supervising programs while Dixon will pay attention to the field installations as institutions.

The reshuffle gave staff instead of line responsibility to the headquarters technical offices. The directors of the nine field centers now report to Seamans and Dixon rather than to the technical offices. Eight of the nine directors remained unchanged. Abe Silverstein, who had been director of space flight programs, was appointed to fill a vacancy at the Lewis Research Center in Cleveland, Ohio.

The most important of the four new technical offices is the Office of Manned Space Flight Programs, which will oversee the spending of between 50 and 60 per cent of the space agency's

NATIONAL AERONAUTICS AND SPACE ADMINISTRATION

ADMINISTRATOR
James E. Webb

DEPUTY ADMINISTRATOR
Hugh L. Dryden

Offices of
Legislative Affairs
Plans & Program Evaluation
Public Affairs

Offices of
General Counsel
International Programs
Executive Assistant

ASSOCIATE ADMINISTRATOR
Robert C. Seamans Jr.

DEPUTY ASSOCIATE ADMINISTRATOR
Thomas F. Dixon

Office of Administration
Albert F. Siepert

Office of Programs
D. D. Wyatt

Office of Advanced Research & Technology
Ira H. Abbott

Office of Space Sciences
Homer E. Newell

Office of Manned Space Flight
D. B. Holmes

Office of Applications

Marshall Space Flight Center Huntsville, Alabama
Wernher von Braun

Ames Research Center Moffett Field, California
S. J. DeFrance

Lewis Research Center Cleveland, Ohio
Abe Silverstein

Flight Research Center Edwards, California
Paul F. Bikle

Manned Spacecraft Center Houston, Texas
Robert R. Gilruth

Goddard Space Flight Center Greenbelt, Maryland
Harry J. Goett

Jet Propulsion Laboratory Pasadena, California (Contractor)
W. H. Pickering

Wallops Station Chinco Teague, Virginia
R. L. Krieger

Langley Research Center Hampton, Virginia
Floyd L. Thompson

budget. Its jurisdiction includes the completion of Project Mercury and all Project Apollo missions from three men in orbit to the landing on the moon. It has complete systems responsibility for Project Apollo—rockets, spacecraft and ground support. The head of the office is D. Brainerd Holmes, who was general manager of the RCA Major Defense Systems Division until he assumed office when the reorganization became effective on November 1, 1961. If he had line responsibility, he would be the man-on-the-moon "czar." However he is officially only an adviser to Seamans.

A second new office, the Office of Applications, supervises the weather and communication satellite programs and helps speed the feedback of practical applications of space technology to the civilian economy. The third new bureau, the Office of Space Sciences, is in charge of unmanned scientific investigations in space and is headed by Homer E. Newell, who was deputy director of the former Office of Space Flight Programs.

The fourth bureau, the Office of Advanced Research and Development, was largely unchanged by the reorganization and remains under the direction of Ira H. Abbott. Its responsibility is to supervise research work not connected with specific projects and to make the considerable technical skills of the agency available for solution of special problems.

Even before completing the major reorganization, Webb approved the creation of a special Office of Programs to help Seamans keep track of the progress of programs and the overall state of the budget. The office is headed by D. D. Wyatt.

The chart on page 211 shows the present NASA organization.

17. BUILDING THE ROCKET

THE APOLLO SPACECRAFT, with three men and sup-
plies to support them, probably will weigh about 12,000 pounds.
But it is not sufficient to build a rocket that will land 12,000
pounds on the moon. Although a permanent base may be established on the moon later on, the first explorers plan to return to
earth after a few days' stay

The lunar landing spacecraft, then, will have to have a rocket
powerful enough to boost it free of the moon and back toward
the earth. Fortunately, the moon's gravity is only a sixth that of
the earth and there is no atmosphere to slow the rocket's progress. Nevertheless, the rocket and fuel to lift the Apollo back off
the moon will weigh almost four times as much as the craft itself.
The spacecraft and return rocket will weigh almost 50,000
pounds altogether. This is more than half as large as the Redstone rocket that launched Alan Shepard and Virgil Grissom on
the first suborbital flights in Project Mercury.

To launch directly from the earth with chemical rockets and
to land any object softly on the moon requires a rocket that
weighs, fully loaded, between 150 and 200 times its payload. It is
not sufficient to launch the payload to velocity of escape from the
earth. When it approaches the moon, the payload must fire another rocket in space to decelerate. Parachutes cannot be used on
the moon because of the lack of a lunar atmosphere. Altogether,
there are five powered phases of the lunar journey, separated by
long coasting periods. First, the lower stages launch Apollo and
the final stages to escape velocity. Next, a mid-course rocket cor-

[213

rects the flight path. Third, a rocket fires several times to slow the fall toward the moon. Fourth a rocket lifts back off again for the return to earth. Finally, a mid-course rocket corrects the flight path, so that the Apollo strikes the atmosphere just at the right point for atmospheric drag to carry it the rest of the way.

The giant rocket for direct ascent to the moon is called Nova. On takeoff, the Nova will weigh about ten million pounds. It will stand about 350 feet tall, two-thirds as tall as the Washington Monument. Its first stage will generate thrust of twelve million pounds, if liquid propellants are used and more than twenty million pounds if solid propellants are used. It will probably consist of five stages.

The first stage of the Nova probably will be a cluster of seven or eight engines, each one of which generates as much thrust as the first stage of the C-1 early model of Saturn. In its liquid-propelled version, the first stage will use conventional fuel, kerosene, and liquid oxygen. The third and fourth stages will use liquid hydrogen and liquid oxygen, as in the upper stages of Saturn. The second stage may use either fuel combination. The fourth stage will be a rocket actually taken over from the Saturn with little change. The final stage will be a small rocket specially designed for the lunar landing and takeoff.

Description of everything required for the Nova requires superlatives. Testing the engines will require mammoth stands. Assembling the rocket will necessitate an enormous factory. Transporting the rocket units will be impossible by highway, rail or air. The factory must therefore be close to the water, so as to provide for water transportation of the units to the launching base. At Cape Canaveral, a tower must be built that will stand almost half as high as the Empire State Building—and it must be movable.

All of these prodigious engineering tasks will require many months of time and many millions of dollars to accomplish. Yet they are just preliminaries to the job of testing and perfecting the rocket system. If Soviet scientists are undertaking a similar project, the job will be just as great for them. Indeed, they may well have to build a rocket even bigger than the Nova to fly to the moon by direct ascent. They have never demonstrated the ability to match the American skill in making miniaturized payloads. Their launching tower might have to be the tallest structure on the Eurasian continent.

The use of liquid hydrogen in the upper stages is an American skill that may in the long run provide an advantage greater than that of miniaturization. Hydrogen fuel delivers at least 30 per cent more "miles per gallon" than kerosene. By converting one stage from kerosene to hydrogen, the effective payload of a liquid rocket stage can be increased by about 50 per cent. If Russia uses kerosene or fuels with similar performance throughout her lunar-landing rocket vehicle, that factor alone would make it necessary that the Russian direct-ascent rocket be more than twice as heavy as Nova.

While there is no assurance that the Russians are not using hydrogen, the odds are against it. If they are doing any extensive work on hydrogen rockets, it has begun rather recently. It seems almost certain that America has a considerable lead in hydrogen research. The discovery that made large hydrogen rockets feasible came from a U.S. government laboratory.

Hydrogen gas must be cooled to the supercold temperature of 423° below zero Fahrenheit—just 36° above absolute zero—before it condenses into a liquid. Manufacturing the liquid on so large a scale is an extremely difficult engineering task in itself. But storage creates an additional problem because liquid hydrogen has a peculiar property. When it first condenses, it assumes an unstable form called orthohydrogen. Later, over a period of days, the liquid gradually changes into a stable form, called parahydrogen. But the conversion releases heat, and as a result, the liquid boils away even when perfectly insulated.

Liquid hydrogen could not be stored in large quantities until someone worked out a method of converting orthohydrogen to parahydrogen at the time of production. In the early 1950s, D. H. Weitzel and W. V. Loebenstein of the Bureau of Standards laboratory at Boulder, Colorado, found a material called hydrous ferric oxide, a purified form of iron rust, that speeded the conversion. Their discovery made it possible for concerns like Air Products Incorporated and the Linde Company to build huge plants in Florida and California that produce liquid hydrogen for rocket fuel use.

There is no reason why Russia could not have made use of the American discovery and developed hydrogen-fueled rockets. The discovery was published by the Bureau of Standards scientists. But it is a normal human trait to prefer familiar ideas, developed within one's own country. It would not be surprising, however, if Russia were also working on them now. But all of the evidence publicly available indicates that the United States is ahead in this particular application.

The two factors in America's favor—miniaturization and liquid hydrogen technology—may well count for more than the Russian lead in rocket development over the six-to-ten-year period of the race for the moon. Thus there is every opportunity for U.S. industrial power to make itself felt and give America a clear victory.

Building the Nova is so stupendous a task that the United States is carrying out two parallel programs of rocket development, in liquid and solid fuels, to provide greater assurance that one or the other will be available when it is needed. While NASA concentrates on liquid rocket work, the Air Force is building large solid-fuel rockets to the space agency's specifications for the first stage. Liquid hydrogen will be used as the fuel in the upper stages of both versions. But whatever is used for the first stage, Nova will take a long time to produce because of its great size.

There are two other possible means of propelling a three-man spacecraft to the moon in which the basic rocket would not be quite so large. If either works, it may make it possible to send the expedition sooner than with the Nova. One possible method is orbital rendezvous and assembly, in which parts of the lunar vehicle are boosted into orbit by the smaller rockets and put together there. The other method is use of a nuclear upper stage. Nuclear propulsion is two to three times as efficient as the most efficient chemical rockets and will make it possible for any given rocket system to carry heavier payloads.

Rendezvous is a risky alternative because the decision on rockets to be used must be made a few years before it is possible to demonstrate that the technique will work. Nuclear propulsion is questionable because the nuclear rocket apparently cannot be developed in time to meet the lunar landing target date. The nuclear vehicle probably can be developed by 1969 or 1970—possibly 1968 if all goes well. But 1967 seems to be too early a target. Regardless of whether it is to be used on the first flight, however, the nuclear vehicle will probably be used for supporting a lunar base and for planetary exploration. Although rendezvous and nuclear propulsion are questionable as individual alternatives, it seems possible that both can make use of the same basic booster

rocket, half the size of Nova. Thus, by developing the smaller
rocket, the United States is covering two bets for the price of one.
But even if it proves possible to send men to the moon with a
smaller rocket, Nova will be built anyway. It will provide
"backup" alternatives for them and it will provide a rocket for
more ambitious missions following the lunar landing. But if the
smaller rocket can be used, it will be possible to slow the Nova
development pace a little and spend a little less money on it.

Presumably, Russia has the same choices as the United States.
The Soviets have a clear lead over the United States in development of large liquid-propelled rockets, however, and would thus
have strong reasons for continuing that route. But Russia also
has an opportunity with the early development of the Vostok-
type spacecraft to develop capability for manned rendezvous in
orbit. Only time can tell whether she will make full use of that
opportunity. The United States, on the other hand, has clear
superiority in solid propulsion and in over-all nuclear technology.

The U.S. liquid propulsion for the lunar landing vehicle will
be based largely on two engines on which development work had
begun before the Kennedy administration decided to go ahead
with the moon venture. The first is the F-1, the largest liquid
engine in the American arsenal, which burns conventional fuels—
liquid oxygen and kerosene. It is designed to produce 1,500,000
pounds of thrust; thus the single F-1 will have thrust equal to
the total of eight engines in the early models of Saturn. The contract for developing the F-1 was awarded in January 1959, but
development will take more than four years. The F-1 is expected
to be ready for flight testing in 1963. Final qualification will
probably take about another year. The first stage of the liquid
Nova will likely be a cluster of eight F-1 engines.

The second basic engine is the J-2, a large unit that capitalizes
on the higher performance gained by burning liquid hydrogen.
It is used both in Nova and in advanced models of Saturn. The
first American liquid hydrogen engine is a smaller one on the
Centaur, which generates 15,000 pounds of thrust. The J-2 is
more than twelve times as large, with 200,000 pounds thrust. In
1962, NASA decided to develop a still larger liquid hydrogen
engine, called M-1, with 1,200,000 pounds of thrust. A cluster
of four M-1 engines is planned for the second stage of Nova.
The third stage is to be a single J-2.

The nature of the final stage of Nova—to be used to slow descent for the lunar landing—may not be decided until 1963. Since it is a relatively small rocket, construction does not require as much time. The NASA propulsion specialists expect to evaluate several rocket systems for reliability before making the selection.

Actually, this final stage is considered a part of the Apollo spacecraft, rather than the launch vehicle. It will not be programmed in advance, but will be turned on and off several times by the Apollo crew as the spacecraft falls toward the moon.

All of the rocket stages must be reliable, but reliability is far more vital in the final stage than in any of the others. If either of the first two stages fail on takeoff, escape rockets will carry the manned Apollo to safety. If the third stage fails, the spacecraft will remain in orbit about the earth, from which it is possible to return. If it performs improperly, the spacecraft may miss the moon and fly out a half-million miles or more into space, but gravity will eventually bring it back to the earth. However, if the final stage fails as the craft is falling toward the moon, there is no escape; it will crash on the moon's surface.

Solid-propellant rockets, if they can be developed in time for use in the Nova first stage, can be expected to be cheaper than those using liquid fuels. The American advantage is based on U.S. superiority in the science and application of organic chemistry. Solid propellants are similar to synthetic rubber and plastics, fields in which American industry leads the world. The fundamental breakthrough in solid propulsion, based on research conducted during and after World War II, took place at Cape Canaveral in March, 1953. If American military and scientific leaders had had the courage to trust in American science and technology, the United States might have used solid propellants to build an ICBM as soon as Russia, despite the Soviet head start. But the leaders suffered from a national inferiority complex and chose instead to rely on German experience with liquid rockets. Part of the delay in developing big liquid rockets resulted from the need for American industry to learn the German techniques before they could go on to larger projects. Eventually they did so, and U.S. industry is now very capable in liquid rocket propulsion. But the nation lost an opportunity to gain time.

A brilliant group of scientists assembled at the Guggenheim

Aeronautical Laboratory, California Institute of Technology (GALCIT), by Theodore von Kármán, a Hungarian-American, laid the groundwork for American superiority in solid propulsion. During the war, they tested dozens of new fuel combinations, and brought forth the idea of a "composite" or mixture of fuel elements. Previously all solid propellants were forms of gunpowder, very unreliable and dangerous to work with because of their explosive properties. The GALCIT researchers chose combinations of chemicals that were not spontaneously combustible, but rather had to be ignited at a fairly high temperature.

Shortly after the war, Charles A. Bartley, one of the GALCIT researchers, invented a process that made possible the 1953 breakthrough. The first composite solid-propellant rockets were limited in size by the stiffness and strength of the rubbery binder material. A propellant charge weighing more than a few hundred pounds would not hold its shape and was subject to cracking and tearing during transportation. It could not be depended upon to burn predictably.

Bartley's contribution was a method of gluing the propellant to the inside of the metal rocket chamber. Thus held in place, much larger solid propellant rockets could be manufactured. The Bartley invention was possible because of a vast amount of research done in the United States during World War II to develop synthetic rubber, because Japanese occupation of Southeast Asia and the East Indies had cut off American supplies of natural rubber. He used a material chemically similar to a constituent of synthetic rubber both as fuel and as the glue that bound the propellant to the chamber wall.

The Army assigned the General Electric Company and Thiokol Chemical Corporation, a small concern in the synthetic rubber supply business, to build the first big solid rocket using the Bartley technique. It contained 5000 pounds of propellant and carried a 1500-pound load of ballast to an altitude of 190,000 feet. "When I saw that thing go, I knew we had made history," said Harold W. Ritchey, a Thiokol engineer. Ritchey said he was certain from that moment that the fundamental problem of travel into space had been solved, that there was no practical limit on the size of a solid-propellant rocket.

But solid-propellant rocket projects moved forward in very slow stages. The Army began development of the Sergeant, a relatively short-range missile, after the 1953 demonstration. It was not until 1956 that a larger rocket was undertaken. The Navy, recognizing the difficulty of dealing with liquid propellants on board a submarine, decided to use solid propulsion for the Polaris, a missile of 1200 miles range. But it was not until 1958 that the Air Force began developing the Minuteman, a solid-propelled ICBM.

The solid-propellant rocket is simpler and thus cheaper than a liquid-propellant rocket because it is a very simple device, with few moving parts. The liquid rocket depends on pumps, valves and tubing to keep the propellant flowing rapidly into the burning chamber. The more powerful the rocket, the more complex the plumbing. The huge F-1, to develop one and a half million pounds of thrust, must pump its liquid propellants into the chamber at a rate of three tons a second.

A big solid rocket is just a boiler-like casing with the fuel glued to the inside and a lengthwise hole in the center. Some sort of igniter shoots a flame the length of the hole. The hot gas from the internal burning shoots out a nozzle or group of nozzles at the bottom. At the top is a covered porthole or group of portholes placed directly opposite the nozzles. When they are opened, the gas flows backward and forward simultaneously, neutralizing the thrust.

Although liquid rockets cost more money and take more time to produce, they provide several advantages over solid rockets. The amount and duration of the thrust can be controlled more precisely by changing the pumping rate, and some liquid rockets can be turned on and off at will. A solid rocket, once cut off, cannot be turned on again. Also, the specific impulse—or miles per gallon—of liquid propellants is higher than solids. A liquid rocket can be pumped full of fuel and test-fired many times. Finally, the liquid propellant can be pumped through the walls of the nozzle to keep it cool. The solid rocket nozzle must use heavy materials specially chosen for high-temperature resistance.

The special advantages of liquid propulsion make them highly desirable for upper stages. The fine control needed for guidance and mid-course corrections can best be achieved with liquid propellants. But the advocates of solid propulsion believe that economy and simplicity will win the battle for them in the huge first stage—and the second stage too, as against kerosene fuel.

The solid rocket, however, has a great deal of time to make up. The development of the big F-1 liquid engine began in early

1959, but the comparable solid-propellant engine had still not begun by late 1961. If the F-1 progress continues on or near schedule, it will probably be chosen for the Nova. But if the F-1 runs into trouble and the solid-propellant engine development proceeds rapidly, the solid will win.

Because of the special advantages of all liquid propulsion and the very high performance of liquid hydrogen, solid propulsion is a candidate only for the first one or two stages of the Nova.

It isn't possible to evaluate the prospects for orbital rendezvous until the United States has developed some experience with the technique. America's first attempts at accomplishing manned rendezvous will not take place until about 1964.

Several possibilities suggest themselves for making use of rendezvous to save time needed to develop the Nova rocket to the degree of perfection required to carry a manned expedition to the moon. A proposed version of Saturn, the C-3, which could be available two years or more earlier than the Nova, might be used to launch parts of the lunar spacecraft into orbit about the earth. The C-3 would have two F-1 engines in its first stage. Three or four such parts could be assembled by rendezvous techniques. Then the vehicle could be launched from orbit. However, accomplishing the tricky job of assembling three or four objects, and possibly filling fuel tanks in orbit, might well take more time than the development of the Nova.

If the rendezvous can be reduced to a job of bringing together two objects, however, it might provide a workable alternative. Milton W. Rosen, NASA launch rocket specialist, has proposed the use of the Nova in its early stages of flight testing, before it has been pronounced sufficiently reliable to risk men's lives. Rosen suggests that the Nova might be used to boost the lunar vehicle into orbit without the Apollo capsule. If the Nova blows up on the pad, no lives are lost. If the launching is a success, the Apollo and its passengers can be boosted into the same orbit with a tried-and-true Saturn. If they fail to achieve rendezvous, they can return to earth and attempt the junction with another Saturn. If they succeed, the rocket combination is assembled for launch from orbit for the moon.

Another means of joining two objects in orbit is by use of a still larger rocket, sometimes called Saturn C-4 and sometimes Nova 4. In its liquid-fueled version, the C-4 or Nova 4 has a first stage consisting of four F-1 engines and total thrust of six million pounds. Two launchings of the C-4 would be necessary for a manned expedition to the moon. First, it would boost into orbit a large, fully fueled rocket stage. Then it would orbit the Apollo spacecraft with the men aboard and the lunar landing and take-off rockets attached. It may, however, be necessary to use a still larger rocket called Saturn C-5, with a five-F-1 first stage.

The two objects would make rendezvous largely by automatic means. But the astronauts aboard the Apollo would be present to monitor the operation and override the automatic equipment in case of malfunction. After confirming that the junction has taken place, successfully, they would wait for computers on the earth below to calculate their orbit and the exact moment they should launch for the moon. If the junction should fail, they could try again or return to the earth.

If neither the solid nor the liquid Nova is ready on schedule, and suitable rendezvous techniques cannot be developed, a vehicle with a nuclear upper stage may be available for a manned lunar flight by 1969 or 1970. Nuclear propulsion is at least twice as efficient as burning hydrogen and oxygen, and it has the capacity to grow steadily more efficient as better materials are developed. It is an absolute must for manned exploration of the planets, and probably will provide a cheaper, more efficient means of transportation to the moon in support of a lunar base.

The form of nuclear propulsion under development in Project Rover does not make direct use of the energy of the atom. Instead, the energy of a nuclear reactor is used to heat a gas, which is expelled out of a nozzle just as in chemical rockets. The gas used is hydrogen, stored in tanks as a liquid, just as in the chemical rockets that burn hydrogen. The difference is that the nuclear rocket needs no supply of oxygen to support combustion, and thus saves a great deal of weight and space occupied by the liquid oxygen. Instead of combustion, the heat is provided by the fission of uranium. Since the nuclear reactor also occupies space and weight, nuclear propulsion makes sense only for a very large rocket, in which the weight of the reactor is less than that of the oxygen it replaces. Nuclear propulsion capitalizes on American technological advantages in two areas—nuclear reactor technology and the use of liquid hydrogen.

The Rover nuclear rocket is a joint project of the space agency and the Atomic Energy Commission. In 1960, a space agency physicist, Harold B. Finger, was assigned responsibility for over-all management. The major milestone of the Rover program will be the first flight test of the first nuclear rocket engine, which will be called NERVA (Nuclear Engine for Rocket Vehicle Application). Present planning calls for the first flight test by 1966. However, Chairman Glenn T. Seaborg of the Atomic Energy Commission believes a 1965 flight may be possible. The first test will be as a second stage atop a Saturn C-1 first stage.

The flight plan calls for a lob shot completely over water. The Saturn stage would carry it above the atmosphere, where the nuclear reactor would be turned on. It would be turned off again before the vehicle enters back into the atmosphere. Thus the hazard of radiation would be negligible. The Nerva could be developed into a third stage of a Saturn, which would double its payload capacity.

For the manned lunar flight, the use of a nuclear third stage could cut the size of the Nova in half. Finger has suggested the use of the same large Saturn, C-4 or C-5, that serves for the rendezvous of two objects.

Heinz Koelle, long-range planner at the space agency's Huntsville rocket center, predicts that a combination of rendezvous and the nuclear rocket will provide the most economic means of large-scale transportation between the earth and the moon. He foresees the journey taking place in three stages: earth to earth orbit, earth orbit to moon orbit and moon orbit to moon surface. For the earth to earth orbit phase, Koelle expects that the Saturn will be the standard truck, and that methods of rocket recovery and re-use will be developed eventually. For the orbit-to-orbit phase, he finds the nuclear rocket most attractive. For the lunar orbit-lunar surface phase, he predicts that a modification of the six-engine S-IV stage of Saturn will be used. Thus, rendezvous is a technique that should be developed even if it is not used for the first lunar landing.

The paraglider, a triangular-shaped wing that is folded between the outer tanks of the Saturn booster during the upward flight, is the cheapest means of recovery. The flow of the air would open the wing like a parachute when the empty rocket falls back. Then it could glide back to the earth. Francis M. Rogallo of the space agency's Langley Aeronautical Laboratory, inventor of the paraglider, got his idea from children's kites. If the method works, it may be possible to save many millions of dollars on each rocket launching by recovering the Saturn first stages and using them again. The process can also be applied to the Nova.

18. THE JOURNEY

IF PROGRESS GOES WELL, a large rocket may be ready by 1965 to launch a three-man Apollo spacecraft on its second mission, a flight around the moon. Before the lunar flight is attempted, the crew will fly the Apollo into a low earth orbit and spend a week there, simulating every step of the journey. Then they will make a practice return to the landing field in the western United States. Later a series of more ambitious flights to increasing altitudes is planned, gradually building up to the flight around the moon.

Besides the danger of rocket failure, there are two known prime hazards in such long space flights. First is weightlessness. Until there is considerable experience with lengthy periods of weightlessness, no one can really promise that it will not cause trouble. The two Mercury Redstone flights by Alan Shepard and Virgil Grissom showed that weightlessness for five to six minutes does not interfere with a man's ability to perform. Yuri Gagarin, in his one-orbit flight, endured weightlessness for almost ninety minutes. Gherman Titov, flying seventeen orbits, was weightless for twenty-five hours.

The Russians have released only sketchy details of how Gagarin and Titov withstood the condition. Gagarin said he had no ill effects, while Titov complained of sensations like seasickness and unpleasant sensations in his inner ear, the organ that controls the sense of balance. Titov slept for more than seven hours during his twenty-five hours in space, but fitfully at first.

When he finally fell soundly asleep, he overslept by thirty-seven minutes. He ate his food, but had very little appetite.

The meager evidence to date thus indicates that, while short periods of weightlessness may be easily bearable, astronauts may encounter difficulty when in space for longer periods. On the other hand, the Titov reaction may be purely individual. The only way to learn for certain is to send other men on the longer flights in earth orbit, from which it is possible to return promptly in case of trouble.

The second difficulty is radiation in space. There are three kinds, cosmic radiation from outside the solar system, radiation from the sun and radiation trapped in belts about the earth. Cosmic radiation is the most powerful of all, but there is so little that it does not constitute a serious danger. From what is now known about the earth's radiation belts, it appears possible to include enough shielding on the Apollo so that it can zip through the dangerous zones on a trip to the moon and back without serious hazard to the men aboard. The Apollo will be designed so that all of its equipment will serve a double purpose. In addition to its primary function, each item will be placed so that it contributes to the shielding against radiation. Water supplies, for example, will be in flat tanks around the surface of the craft. The stringent weight limits, however, will allow very little dead metal placed just for shielding. Thus the radiation from the sun will be a prime hazard. The spacecraft will not have enough shielding to protect the men against a cloud of high-energy protons spewed out by a major solar flare.

The Apollo flight plan is to scoot for home if a solar flare appears. For the flight around the moon, more than half of the spacecraft's weight is fuel for on-board rockets. Even so, if a solar flare occurs while the Apollo is halfway to the moon, after burning all the fuel it will still take almost two days to get back to the earth. The rockets will merely slow the upward progress, so that the craft does not reach all the way to the moon and falls back. However, a solar cloud takes more than a day to reach the earth after a flare.

The lunar flights will have to depend on a system of solar weather forecasting. One of the most promising methods is being developed by Kinsey Anderson of the State University of Iowa. By studying sunspots, Anderson believes he can predict with fairly high certainty when a solar flare will *not* occur within the next few days. Other scientists have detected apparent relationships between jigglings in the earth's magnetic field and solar flares. Hopefully, the scientists will have developed reliable techniques for predicting solar activity by 1965. Their help will be sorely needed because the sun will be heading into another active period. The height of the last solar cycle was 1957-58. The next is due eleven years later, in 1968-69.

On the way to the lunar vicinity, the astronauts, aided by automatic guidance and control equipment, will keep close watch on their flight trajectory. They will have plenty of fuel in their on-board rockets to correct the flight path several times. Their initial speed will be just short of that required for escape from the earth. If they were not planning to stop at the moon, it would carry them out a half-million miles or more before they fell back to the earth.

Therefore, as they approach the moon, they will fire rockets to reduce speed enough to allow the moon to capture their ship as a satellite, orbiting at from 50 to 100 miles altitude in a period of about two hours. As they swing around, they will look at possible landing areas. There will be automatic equipment already on the moon that has been sent ahead of them—first the Rangers and then the Surveyors. By visual observation of the areas from low lunar orbit, they will be able to decide which region seems most likely.

The explorers may also be able to help interpret some of the information telemetered by the automatic equipment on the lunar surface. It seems highly unlikely that the Rangers and Surveyors will all operate perfectly; some of the data is bound to be erratic. By flying over the area and observing the terrain, they may be able to figure out what went wrong.

After two or three turns around, the Apollo is ready to head for home. At a carefully calculated moment, the rockets will fire once more to enable the Apollo to escape from the lunar gravity. Then it will begin the long fall back to the earth. Some fuel will remain in the rocket for mid-course correction. Guidance is an extremely tricky problem on the return journey because the ship must enter a narrow layer of the earth's outer atmosphere. If it hits too high, it will swing out on a wide orbit through the radiation belts again. If it hits too low, the "g" forces and the heat of entry may be too much for the astronauts. As in the return through the atmosphere from the orbital mission, the craft will be maneuverable because of the modest amount of aerodynamic lift provided by the spacecraft's shape. Control tabs, like the rudder and ailerons of an airplane, will again enable the Apollo to change its flight path.

Will Russian astronauts fly around the moon first? Quite possibly. Some U.S. observers speculate that Russia is developing a "Saturn" eight-cylinder rocket made up of their basic R-14A engine, of 265,000 pounds thrust. Such a Russian Saturn thus would have takeoff thrust of about 2,100,000 pounds. With suitable upper stages, that rocket could launch a Vostok on a circumlunar flight, with fuel for maneuvering in space. However, such a flight would be conducted with very narrow margins of safety. There would not be as much fuel to make for home as in the American Apollo, which will be boosted by a Saturn C-4 or C-5 with at least six or seven million pounds of thrust. The Russian craft probably could not carry a crew of more than two. However, the rugged construction of the Vostok would provide adequate shielding for all but the worst solar flares. The sun is expected to be quiet in the 1963-64 period. Improvements will be needed on the Vostok, of course. Insulation must be provided to protect it against the heat of return from the moon at a speed of 25,000 miles an hour, almost half again as fast as return from orbital flight. And a larger model may have to be built to accommodate two men on a seven-day journey. But I believe the Soviets may be able to modify the Vostok and build the bigger rocket by 1963 or 1964, a time when the sun will be quiet. If so, they may take the chance of sending a manned flight around the moon without radiation shielding or fuel to race for home.

The American circumlunar rocket, becoming available perhaps two years later, will have a greater payload capacity and thus will provide the possibility of a more sophisticated mission. The scientific observer aboard will make it possible for the Americans to learn more on their flight. Nevertheless, the Russians may well win again in the battle for the prestige of being first. However, although the Russians have an advantage in this race, it is not large. If American progress picks up speed and the Russians run into any difficulty, Apollo astronauts will have a chance to make this trip first.

But the landing on the moon is a big step beyond the circumlunar flight. There is no evidence publicly available that Soviet Russia had begun work on her version of the giant Nova before

1961—although, like the United States, Russia undoubtedly was working on a large single liquid-fueled engine. As I have already indicated, the Soviet launching rocket probably will have to be larger than the American Nova, and, despite the superior Soviet know-how in building large rockets, may take longer to develop. No one really knows, of course, just when the Soviet development began. But unless it began two years or more before the American start in 1961, the Russian advantage is very small. If America and Russia began at about the same time, the United States must have an advantage on the basis of overall industrial and scientific capacity.

Thus we must raise the question whether the Soviet government will really make the race. Reorganization and marshaling of national resources must also be necessary there. Soviet scientists in the past have stated their government's intention to explore the moon and the planets. But as the effort grows, the strain on the Soviet economy will be great. Unlike the United States, Russia has no problem of surplus production capacity. Resources applied to national projects like space exploration must ultimately be diverted from the consumer economy—and this during a period when Khrushchev is promising great advances in the Soviet standard of living.

There could be a temptation, if the United States pulls ahead, for Russia to chuck the whole business, reverse the party line and declare that exploring space is a lot of foolishness. However, such an eventuality is probably unlikely. Even a totalitarian state would find it difficult to reverse itself so fundamentally. Khrushchev is too deeply committed to space exploration. Yet if the United States pulls ahead the Soviets may well be willing to cooperate on joint U.S.-Soviet projects. At this stage, it is difficult to imagine how joint projects might be organized technically. The problem of mating parts made on opposite sides of the world, with different technologies, might be almost insuperable. But if there were a will, the scientists could probably find a way. The history of the International Geophysical Year and the exploration of Antarctica give evidence that scientists of East and West can work together on occasion. However, the realities of international politics indicate that the two will probably conduct separate moon expeditions, and will be in a neck-and-neck race for the honor of landing first.

Two or three American crews will probably reconnoiter the

vicinity in flights around the moon while waiting for the availability of propulsion for the landing. The scientist-observers will most likely be geologists, with considerable knowledge about meteorites. The first things to be learned will involve the nature of the surface rocks and soil. But the observer on the landing mission must also have familiarity with the state of knowledge and the experimental equipment used in several branches of geophysics. He must measure magnetic fields, radiation and gravity, as well as operate devices to take moonquake readings. He must be able to repair television and other electronic equipment. He must be familiar with astronomy, so as to make observations of the stars and planets. He must have some knowledge of biology, to take specimens of possible rudimentary forms of life on the moon.

The two pilot-astronauts will be trained in the operation of all the scientific instruments, so that they can help him in his work during the stay on the moon. And the scientific observer, of course, will be needed for the countdown in preparation for lunar takeoff.

Space agency scientists have already chosen a tentative lunar landing area, called the Oceanus Procellarum. It is in the part of the moon that is sunlit during the last quarter, southwest of a prominent crater called Copernicus. But it would be surprising if, after six or seven years of lunar research, that choice should stand up. However, the Ranger unmanned flights beginning in 1962 will be aimed at the Oceanus Procellarum. Depending on what is learned in the Ranger flights, the Surveyors may follow the next year. Eventually, a considerable store of equipment and supplies will be shipped to the landing area on unmanned rockets before the manned landing. The present plan is to develop a large unmanned spacecraft called Prospector, to be launched from the earth by Saturn, to deliver the supplies. One version of the Prospector will carry a two-wheel electrically driven vehicle that will be operated by remote control from the earth to explore the lunar terrain up to fifty miles from the point of landing. The astronauts will be able to take over control of the Prospector vehicles after they land.

The American flight will take off from Cape Canaveral at a time of the month when the crescent moon is about a week past its last quarter and approaching the new moon phase. The target area in Oceanus Procellarum will still be sunlit, but the sun will be due to set within about three days. Halfway to the moon, the Apollo will fire an on-board rocket for the first time, to correct the course. A second firing, near the end of the sixty-hour journey, will reduce speed enough that the spacecraft will be captured in a lunar orbit, the purpose of which is to establish the position and flight path more exactly in reference to the moon. After the lunar orbit is observed and calculated exactly, the amount and timing of the third rocket firing can be calculated, so that the craft can land at the desired point. Such calculations cannot be made with a slide rule and a set of tables, of course. Complex computing equipment must be carried, and there will be constant radio communication with earth bases, which will have access to even more elaborate computers. However, practical considerations will require that much of the calculation must be done on board. Thus all crew members, but particularly the co-pilot-navigator, must be able to operate the on-board computers.

Small gas jets will turn the Apollo into just the proper attitude for firing a rocket to reduce the orbital speed so it will fall toward the lunar surface. A short time before landing, another rocket will fire to enable the craft to hover thirty or forty feet above the surface before it falls the final distance and lands on tripods, near an area where Prospector-shipped supplies can be seen. Since the moon's gravity is only about a sixth as great as at the earth's surface, a fall from thirty to forty feet will strike at the speed of an earthly fall of five to seven feet. The "hover" rocket must be the most reliable of all. If a rocket fails at any other step of the journey, the astronauts have a chance to escape or try again. But the hover rocket must work the first time. Thus the high performance of liquid hydrogen fuel will be sacrificed if necessary for reliability and simplicity. The hover rocket will probably use liquid fuels of a type that ignites spontaneously on contact.

One of the possible dangers on landing is that the spacecraft may fall into a deep sea of dust and sink below the surface. The current scientific opinion is that dust covers many of the flat surfaces of the moon. However, few scientists believe the dust is that deep. Meteors falling upon the lunar surface create the dust by chipping away at the surface of rocks and other hard objects. At first, the prevailing opinion was that the dust ought to remain right where the meteors strike. But a few years ago, Thomas Gold of Cornell University pointed out that protons from solar flares hitting the moon's surface could give most of the dust particles a positive electric charge. Since objects with similar electric charge repel each other, the dust particles flow apart, gradually sliding into the lunar lowlands.

The sun itself is the greatest hazard. At the lunar equator, the sun heats the temperature of the surface above 200° Fahrenheit when it is in the sky above. The sun also is a source of energetic particles, X-rays, ultraviolet and other dangerous radiation. This is why the first expedition will plan to land when the sun is low on the horizon or has already set. The moon keeps one face always toward the earth and rotates in twenty-nine days, the same period that it takes to revolve around the earth. The lunar day thus lasts two weeks.

Landing in the last day or two of the sunlit period, the explorers will find the surface will have cooled to a bearable degree. They will plan to remain several days, or perhaps a week, after the sun has set. During all this time, the surface will be cooling rather rapidly. At its coldest, a short time before sunrise, parts of the lunar surface fall to a temperature of more than 200° below zero. This fact does not disturb the spacecraft engineers, however, since it is always easier to provide heat than refrigeration.

Nor is the lack of sunlight a serious problem during the two-week lunar night. The earth, high in the sky, will provide light enough for the explorers to see their way about the surface. When the moon is new, it is approximately between the sun and the earth. Thus, looking from the moon, the earth will appear to be "full" and there will be a maximum amount of earthlight.

By landing just before the sun sets over the western horizon, the explorers will have a chance to observe a phenomenon ordinarily seen on earth only during a total eclipse of the sun. Just after the sun sets, they will be able to examine the sun's corona, which extends up to fourteen million miles out beyond the visible disk, but is normally invisible because the visible disk is so much brighter. The moon rotates so slowly that the visible disk will take about an hour to sink below the horizon. The corona will remain visible for perhaps fifteen hours after sunset—long enough to study it in detail. A view of the corona above a lunar mountain range must be one of the most beautiful sights in the solar system.

Right after sunset will be the time to take the first venture out onto the lunar surface. In the nose of the Apollo will be an airlock. Dressed in his space suit, the scientist-observer will climb into the lock and check the suit, oxygen supply, power, radio, heating pads and other gear. Then the air will be pumped out of the lock to a container in another part of the spacecraft and he can open the hatch and climb out.

He probably will be carrying a kit of small digging tools, a set of numbered small bags and a notebook and pencil. A ball-point pen wouldn't do because the ink would dry rapidly in the lunar vacuum. He will wander about, probably staying within a few hundred feet of the ship, picking up samples and making notes on the nature of the soil. His two companions will remain in the craft supervising his investigation and constantly communicating with the earth. Probably the pilot commander will be talking with the explorer and observing the telemetry from his space suit, while the copilot-navigator will operate the radio communications to the earth.

What will it be like to walk about the moon's surface? A 160-pound man will weigh just over 26 pounds on the moon. With the effort it would require to jump three feet into the air on earth, he could jump to a height of eighteen feet above the lunar surface. If he wanted to run back to the ship in an emergency, he might find himself taking great leaping strides of twenty, or perhaps even forty feet.

Since the moon has no atmosphere, the sky will be black, just as in space. Many more stars will be visible than from the earth. The lunar sky will be dominated, of course, by the earth, a huge white globe with patches of light blue, green and yellow, and possibly a trace of red-orange above the poles. Since the earth's diameter is almost four times as great as the moon, the earth will be an object in the lunar sky with almost four times as great an apparent diameter as the moon has from the earth.

The view on the moon will depend on where the ship lands. The moon has mountains and great flat plains, presumably covered with dust. But wherever he stands, the explorer will have a sense that the horizon is very near, because the lunar surface is curved almost four times as much as that of the earth. In an area without mountains or valleys, a man walking away would disappear below the lunar horizon in about 8500 feet, less than two miles.

On the first forays onto the lunar surface, the explorer will remain close to the ship, where he can be seen by his comrades, who will be able to come to his aid promptly in case of emergency. He will certainly not venture beyond the horizon. The problem is not merely visibility. Radio communication will also be impossible beyond the lunar horizon. On earth, some radio waves are reflected by the ionosphere. On the moon, all wavelengths presumably will carry only as far as straight-line travel will take them. Thus one of the first tasks of the lunar explorers will be to erect a tall radio tower to enable them to transmit longer distances.

However, the value of towers will be limited. A 25-foot tower would add about three miles to the range over which an explorer could communicate with his base. Building towers much taller than that would hardly make the effort worthwhile. Even a tower standing 1000 feet, as tall as the Empire State Building, would extend the range only twenty miles. The explorer can increase his radio range somewhat by carrying a portable antenna that he could extend five feet or so above his head. With a portable antenna extending ten feet high, and a tower 25 feet tall at the ship, the explorer could go more than five miles and yet remain within radio range. Beyond that, a relay would probably be necessary. A portable automatic radio relay station could be set down at maximum range from the ship and then the explorer could go beyond and remain within range.

Another possibility is relay from the earth. If one of the powerful deep-space antennas at Goldstone, California; Woomera, Australia; or Krugersdorp, South Africa, is facing the moon, it may be able to pick up the radio signal from the explorer in his space suit and rebroadcast it back to the ship. That method would provide communications all across the face of the moon visible from the earth. Earth relay would have the disadvantage that the message would have to travel almost a half-million miles. Even at the speed of light, the trip takes three seconds. It might be an eerie sensation for the lunar explorer, waiting six seconds for a reply from his comrades a few miles away, to realize how far his voice must travel.

Besides geological investigation, one job of the early explorers will be to examine the condition of the automatic scientific equipment that has been sent ahead of them. Some of the unmanned stations will have landed too far away to reach them on foot. However, others may be close enough so that an explorer will be able to get there without leaving the circle of radio range.

Another task will be to gather together all the supplies and equipment that have been rocketed on ahead. Some of these will also be too far afield. But we can hope that most will be within range. One of the packages may contain a large, plastic inflatable dome, which can be opened to make the first house for men on the surface of the moon. It will have to have at least two walls to provide insurance that holes produced by accident or perhaps meteors would not cause loss of air to the vacuum outside. Airlocks will also have to be fixed to the doors.

Putting up the dome will probably be a heavy job for two of the three explorers. On the first trip, at least one of them will undoubtedly remain aboard ship at all times as a safety precaution. The work will be made easier, however, by the low lunar gravity. After the dome is erected, they will start moving equipment inside—air supplies, kitchen, sanitary facilities, heating units, radio and scientific instruments. Electric power supplies will also be needed. In the beginning, the power source will probably be batteries, with solar cells to be stationed outside the dome to recharge the batteries during the two-week lunar day. But if a lunar base is established, its power requirements will grow to the point at which shipment of a nuclear reactor power supply to the moon would be cheaper than shipping batteries and solar cells.

After the explorers have investigated the terrain, checked the scientific instruments and set up rudimentary living quarters— over a period of perhaps a week—it will be time to return to earth. They will leave behind all their equipment and supplies designed for use on the moon, carrying back only enough for the return journey. They will also bring a set of samples of the lunar rocks and soil for analysis in earth laboratories. The observer geologist will have some lightweight instruments to make preliminary analyses on the moon, so as to make certain he does not bring back a lot of samples that are duplicates of one another.

Taking off for the return from the moon is probably the most difficult task of the expedition. The rocket that lifts off the lunar surface is more than half as large as the Mercury-Redstone rocket. Almost a hundred men were needed to supervise the Redstone flights from Cape Canaveral on the ground. The trick will be for the three men inside the Apollo capsule to conduct a similar countdown.

There will be no need for the rocket to point upward on the

moon. On earth, the rocket points upward to get above the atmosphere as soon as possible so as to get away from atmospheric drag. With no atmosphere, there is no drag on the moon. Thus the takeoff from the moon will be in the more natural horizontal position. The hover rocket will lift the vehicle a few feet above the lunar surface, then the main rockets will propel it forward to the speed of 7800 feet per second needed to escape from the moon's gravity. Guidance to the earth is a somewhat less difficult problem than hitting the moon because earth gravity takes the Apollo in tow after it has traveled only one eightieth of the way home. But there is still the problem of hitting the atmosphere at just the proper angle. Fortunately, the explorers have already learned how to manage this on earlier flights.

As I have tried to show the first flight to the moon will be a very dangerous journey. Pitfalls beset the explorers at every step of the way there and back. And so every precaution will have to be taken to reduce the danger—by sending out instrumented probes in advance, by sending supplies ahead, by rehearsing the whole journey in orbit and by exhaustively testing the rockets and spacecraft. But despite all precautions, unexpected events are bound to occur and unexpected conditions seem certain to be encountered. The reason for the journey is the uncertainty. Thus we must anticipate the possibility that some lunar explorers will lose their lives, just as others have died while exploring inhospitable parts of the earth.

19. BUILDING A BASE

AN'S FIRST VISIT to the moon will not be his last. Eventually, scientists will establish a permanent station there, just as they have at the South Pole. The environment of the moon is much more hostile than at the Pole and the propulsion requirement makes it much harder to reach. But the opportunity to make scientific observations is correspondingly greater.

The greatest opportunity is in astronomy. Earth-bound astronomers, even on a cloudless night, must peer through an atmosphere that makes all their pictures fuzzy. In the lunar vacuum, a telescope 50 inches in diameter can see as well and as far as the 200-inch telescope at Palomar, the world's largest, in the wavelengths of visible light. But many kinds of radiation—in the infrared, ultraviolet, X-ray and radio wavelengths—are completely absorbed by the atmosphere. Astronomers' only knowledge of the sun, stars, planets, comets and so forth in those wavelengths comprises a few tantalizing bits of information gathered by rockets and satellites.

In late 1963 or 1964, the United States plans to launch the first Orbiting Astronomical Observatory in an effort to gain more such information from space. It is impossible to predict in advance, of course, the success of such an effort. But it does seem reasonable to assume that a complex unmanned satellite operating by remote control from the earth will not be as effective as if trained men were aboard to operate it. We can also assume that one of the greatest problems will be to maintain a steady orientation for the satellite telescope so it can photograph the stars.

A possible solution to the first problem would be to install the astronomical observatory aboard a large manned space station. But that would just raise a new question about weightlessness. We suspect already that all men do not withstand prolonged weightlessness equally. And so it might be necessary for such a station to spin like a top to create an artificial gravity. Spinning the station would introduce new engineering problems in maintaining the telescope orientation.

All things considered, a base on the moon will probably prove to be a more desirable location for a permanent manned observatory. Lunar gravity, even though only a sixth that of earth, will make conditions comfortable, and the firm foundation will eliminate the problem of stabilizing the telescope's orientation.

But before they have time to set up large telescopes, pioneers must make the moon habitable. In the beginning, of course, all supplies—air, water, food, tools, building materials and equipment—must be shipped from the earth. Economical means must be developed for large-scale transportation. The best in prospect is the nuclear rocket under development in Project Rover. But it might be more efficient to use the nuclear energy directly, or to convert it into electrical energy.

Nuclear physicists are investigating many such schemes and it is possible one that has not even been yet imagined may provide the solution. One method of direct conversion of energy would use small nuclear bombs for propulsion. The idea is under study in an Air Force project called Orion. Because of the fallout from nuclear explosions, the United States does not plan to test any such system in the atmosphere. However, the possibility remains that such a rocket might be used in outer space after being launched from the earth by chemical means.

A more immediate use of nuclear energy is to provide large quantities of electrical power, which in turn is converted into thrust. All electrical propulsion devices generate very low thrust in relation to their weight and thus would be unable to lift off the surface of the earth or the moon. However, their specific impulse is very high; that is, they provide a large amount of propulsion with a small amount of fuel—more miles per gallon.

Two kinds of electrical propulsion are fairly near reality—ion rockets and arc jets. In the first ion rockets to be tested, the fuel is a liquid metal, either cesium or mercury. With an arc jet, the fuel is hydrogen or ammonia. In both devices, electrical energy accelerates the fuel from the nozzle at high speed. The ion rocket has the highest specific impulse—perhaps twenty times as great as chemical rockets—but its thrust is usually not more than 1/10,000 of the total mass of the rocket and payload. The arc jet thrust may be five times higher. It may reach 1/2000 of the total mass, but its specific impulse is only three or four times that of chemical rockets.

Accelerating a large spacecraft from earth orbit to moon orbit might take as much as five months with an early-model ion rocket, while an early-model arc jet might do the job in one month. Neither could be used for manned spacecraft. High-thrust chemical and nuclear rockets could make the journey in two and a half days. But for freight, the shipment time is unimportant if the vehicle is not manned. If the electrical rockets prove less expensive, they will be preferred. However, the five-month journey of the ion rocket might impose performance, reliability and guidance requirements that would be hard to meet. Thus the arc jet, which would consume four times as much fuel, might be preferred for the lunar mission.

The very high specific impulse of the ion rocket, on the other hand, may make it a perfect form of propulsion for transportation beyond the moon. It still has not been demonstrated, however, that an ion rocket will actually work in outer space. NASA planned a joint flight test of two types of ion rocket for late 1962 on a long suborbital lob shot boosted by a Scout rocket with engines powered by batteries. Arc jets will be flight-tested later. By 1965, a nuclear reactor designed to supply 30 to 60 kilowatts of power will be available for a joint orbital test of an ion rocket of 1/10-pound thrust and an arc jet with thrust of a half-pound. The reactor, called SNAP 8 (Systems for Nuclear Auxiliary Power), is one of a series of projects to produce electricity from nuclear energy in outer space and remote sections of the earth. The first nuclear space device, a small radioisotope electric power supply for the Navy's Transit IV-A navigation satellite, was launched June 29, 1961.

If a nuclear-electric rocket is used for shipping supplies to the moon, the transportation system probably will be in conjunction with rendezvous and transfer at two levels, orbit about the earth and orbit around the moon. The scheme will thus be similar to that worked out by Heinz Koelle for transporting passengers, except that the nuclear-electric rocket will replace the nuclear rocket in the orbit-to-orbit phase. Chemical rockets such as Saturn will lift the payload into earth orbit to meet the electrically propelled ferry. If the ferry has made several round trips to the moon, it may also be necessary to load it up with fuel. After the long trip, a manned rocket lifts from the lunar base to make a junction with the ferry in orbit about the moon. Then, like a tugboat in an earth harbor, the two return to the moon base and unload their supplies.

Shipping supplies from the earth will be so expensive that the lunar pioneers will seek as soon as practicable to make their colony at least partially self-sufficient. The early shipments will include seeds of many kinds for experiments to learn what sort of plant life can grow indoors in the lunar soil. All vegetation consumes carbon dioxide and releases oxygen, thus reducing the need of oxygen supplies and chemical treatments of the stale air. And of course some vegetation can provide food. The plants will require water, which will probably be scarce and may be nonexistent on the moon. The pioneers' water will have to be used repeatedly. Urine will be recycled. Means will probably be found also for the re-use of other body wastes.

But the most important way the colony can become self-supporting is to find usable resources on the moon. The pioneers will prospect for ores—not precious metals or even uranium at first. Rather they will seek common materials from which oxygen, water and rocket fuel can be extracted. Of the three, rocket fuel is potentially the most useful. Fuel comprises more than half of the weight of a chemical rocket such as will be used for transfer between the moon and lunar orbit, both for men and freight. If it can be produced on the moon, it will reduce by a considerable amount the supplies that must be shipped from the earth.

Setting up a chemical processing plant on the moon may prove to be a difficult task, but well worth the effort. One problem, that of electric power, can be solved fairly easily. A compact nuclear reactor, such as is being developed in the SNAP programs, can be sent to the moon to provide for the regular needs of the pioneers as well as the power required to operate the chemical plant. With adequate power, ores can be reduced by electrolysis. We do not know what minerals will be found, and thus we cannot predict what fuels will be extractable. The most desirable would be hydrogen and oxygen, but it remains to be seen whether either will be available in quantity. There is no evidence that water exists on the moon. Water vapor, like most gases, escapes into space because the speed of its molecules is greater than that required to overcome the lunar gravity. However, it may be possible to extract water from rocks near the moon's north and south poles.

While the lunar pioneers are developing the capacity to support themselves, the supply line from the earth will be difficult and expensive to maintain. But the supply job will not involve any major scientific or engineering developments. Once the first lunar explorers have perfected the technique of getting there and back, building up the base will be to some extent a matter of mass production. Thus, even if Soviet astronauts should win the race for the first lunar landing, the superior productive capacity of the American economy can soon build up a scientific station much larger and better equipped than any Soviet station. If not sooner, the world will certainly know by then who leads in space exploration.

Russia launched the first satellite in 1957 but within the next four years the United States launched three times as many satellites and deep-space probes as the Soviet Union. Russia launched the first man into space but the United States, in Project Mercury, has plans to launch several men into orbit. The United States may well put more men on the moon than Russia. When the time comes for low-cost tours of outer space and the moon, they will undoubtedly be organized by an American company.

And if anything on the moon should turn out to have military value, the United States will be in a position to prevent its being used by a potential enemy.

SECTION

V THE FUTURE

20. THE PLANETS AND BEYOND

VENUS AND MARS, the nearest of the nine planets that circle our sun, are very far away. Neither comes as close as a hundred times the distance to the moon. There is no reason to doubt that men will visit them some day, probably well before the end of this century. But the preparations for such a journey will take many years. Flying to the moon makes it possible, however, to develop the necessary skill in easy stages. The relatively short trip is something like the beginners' slope at a ski center. When men have become proficient in flying to the moon and back, they can then attempt the far more difficult flights to the planets.

All the planets are of tremendous interest to science. Venus and Mars are of special importance, not only because they are nearest but because if life exists anywhere in the solar system other than here it most likely will be found on one of those two. Venus, Planet No. 2 and the nearest of all, is in many ways the most mysterious—a riddle wrapped in an enigma wrapped in dense white clouds. Astronomers cannot say whether the surface below is all desert or all ocean. They are ignorant about the composition of the atmosphere, including the clouds themselves. They are uncertain about the surface temperature—although it seems to be quite hot. They are not sure whether Venus rotates, or if it does, how fast. If Venus' surface is anywhere nearly as hot as some recent measurements indicate, life probably cannot exist there. But until it is possible to take a closer look, the evidence will remain indecisive.

[243

More is known about Mars, the fourth planet, whose atmosphere is mostly transparent. Although Mars is much colder than the earth and astronomers have found no trace of oxygen, there is fairly strong evidence of vegetable life in dark surface patches, which wax and wane with the seasons. In the absence of oxygen, it is hard to imagine how animal life could exist. That question must also remain open, however, until someone can investigate at first hand.

But first-hand investigation of Venus and Mars is even more difficult than on the moon, whose conditions, although inhospitable, are not very different from outer space itself. The problem of supporting explorers on the moon is similar to that of maintaining them during space flight. Both Venus and Mars, however, can be expected to make new demands of the life support gear—Venus because of the heat and possibly the atmosphere; Mars because of the intense cold. Furthermore, the propulsion required for takeoff will have to overcome a gravitational field far greater than that of the moon. Landing, however, might be easier than on the moon if the planetary atmosphere can be used to slow the spacecraft.

Unmanned spacecraft will probe the planets long before men travel there, of course. In the early 1960s, the United States will launch Venus and Mars probes under a project called Mariner. Venus will be in position for a launching in August, 1962, and at intervals of nineteen months thereafter. Mars will be in position in November, 1962, and every twenty-five months afterward.

A Mariner flight will be simply a probe of the general neighborhood of a planet. Scientific instruments aboard will observe conditions in interplanetary space and the changes that take place as the craft approaches the planet. By bringing instruments close, it should be possible to make more accurate measurements than are possible from the earth. Later, when the Saturn rockets become available for interplanetary investigations, Project Voyager will launch much larger spacecraft, which will carry propulsion enough to maneuver into orbit about the planet. American technology has made great strides toward solving the problems of communication over such vast distances.

Although Venus and Mars are so far away, flight to the vicinity of either is not much more of a propulsion task than flight to the vicinity of the moon. Once an object has left the earth's gravity, it becomes a little planet revolving about the

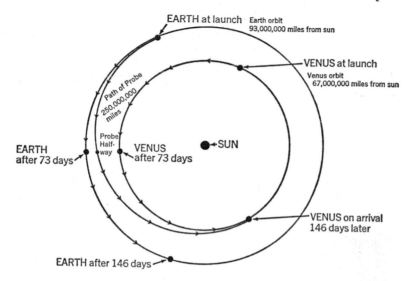

EARTH at launch Earth orbit
93,000,000 miles from sun

VENUS at launch
Venus orbit
67,000,000 miles from sun

Path of Probe
250,000,000 miles

Probe Half-way

EARTH after 73 days

VENUS after 73 days

SUN

VENUS on arrival
146 days later

EARTH after 146 days

sun. A relatively small change in orbital speed will nudge it into another orbit, along a path that diverges slightly from its previous path. Eventually, the two paths spread wide apart. If we figure the spread correctly, we can arrange things so that the object's path eventually will cross that of another celestial body.

Thus we can make the object travel very far away with a relatively small application of energy. But because of the vast distance it must travel, guidance is a much more critical problem than propulsion. Things would be bad enough if the travel could be in a straight line. Venus, at its nearest pass, is 26,-000,000 miles from the earth. The minimum distance to Mars is 49,000,000 miles. But a practicable flight to either planet could not be in anything like a straight line. The earth travels more than eighteen miles per second in its orbit around the sun. For an object to turn a right angle and head straight for Venus or Mars would require an enormous amount of energy and thus an impossibly large amount of fuel. Another equally large amount of energy would be needed to turn again to match the planet's orbital speed. But the trip can be made with comparatively little energy if we take advantage of the fact that the earth and both its neighbors are hurtling around the sun at high speeds in the same direction, like trains on parallel tracks.

For minimum energy expenditure, we must time the trip when the earth and the target planet are due to pass close together. On a flight to Venus, for example, the spacecraft would turn slightly inward toward the sun, so as to follow an orbit that touches the earth's orbit at the beginning and Venus' orbit at its destination. Such a journey would last 146 days and would cover 250 million miles—ten times the distance that separated Venus and the earth at their nearest passage, which would take place when the spacecraft is at the halfway point. The diagram on page 245 will show what I mean.

Some travel time can be saved without great expense in energy. On February 12, 1961, a Soviet rocket launched a probe toward Venus on a trajectory that was to require only ninety-seven days instead of the least-energy 146. This was done by shooting the craft away from the earth at a little over 1000 feet per second more than the bare minimum. Nevertheless, that trip still covered 160 million miles. The Soviet Venus probe's radio failed a short time after it left the earth and so no one really knows where it went. But the laws of physics insist that, if its initial course was correct and unless it hit a meteor, it must have gone to the vicinity of Venus. On a 160,000,000-mile journey, however, the miss may well have been several million miles. If men are to travel to Venus, guidance and control equipment must be more accurate than for the lunar flight. However, the duration of the journey provides plenty of time for repeated mid-course correction.

On a round trip to Venus, the travelers must carry supplies for almost two years. For it isn't possible to turn around and fly right back to the earth after a short reconnaissance of the second planet. The earth will be out of position and the explorers will have to wait until the next passage.

It is clear that the manned planetary spacecraft must be very large and heavy. Supplies and life support equipment for the long journey will use a great deal of weight. The guidance equipment will be complex. And if a landing is to be attempted, bulky landing gear and huge takeoff rockets must be carried. Thus we return to a stupendous propulsion assignment—the transportation of these large loads. For interplanetary travel, the chemical rocket drops completely out of the running. So far as we can predict now, the competition is between the nuclear rocket, which pumps liquid hydrogen through the bowels of a supercritical reactor, and the nuclear-electric rocket, which uses the heat of the reactor to generate power, electrify some kind of fuel and use electrical forces to drive the fuel out the nozzle at high speed. I should make it clear that the competition is on the orbit-to-orbit phase of the journey. Large chemical and nuclear rockets will doubtless remain the most practical means of obtaining the high thrust necessary for escaping from the earth's gravity. It is idle to speculate on the means of landing on and takeoff from Venus or Mars until we know more about the nature of atmosphere, radiation belts and other local conditions.

The difference between the nuclear and nuclear-electric rockets for interplanetary travel is in thrust and fuel economy. The nuclear rocket develops fairly high thrust but has lower fuel economy. Because of its high thrust, however, the trip is somewhat shorter than by electric rocket, which gives more miles per gallon.

One kind of electric rocket, the ion rocket, has the lowest thrust and highest fuel economy of all. The journey by ion rocket would probably be a month or two longer than by nuclear rocket.* Flight by ion rocket would have one other interesting property. The travelers would not be completely weightless, since the rocket provides constant thrust for the duration of the trip. However, the thrust is so low that it would accelerate the spacecraft only about 1/10,000 as much as does Earth's gravity. Therefore, the space travelers would feel a weight 1/10,000 as great as normal. A 160-pound man would weigh about a quarter of an ounce. The weight, though tiny, would help keep loose objects in place aboard the spacecraft. And, conceivably, it might have beneficial psychological effects. The travelers would be able to sense the directions of up and down.

Orbital rendezvous, assembly and launching will be essential, whatever means of propulsion is chosen for interplanetary travel. A spacecraft for the trip to Venus or Mars, launched from orbit, might weigh upwards of a million pounds. A rocket to launch such a payload from the earth would have to be many times as large as Nova. The obvious alternative, using techniques that ought to be fully developed by the time we are ready to explore

---

* Electric-rocket specialists believe that an advanced model of ion rocket will develop higher thrust, making possible a journey of about the same duration as by nuclear rocket.

the planets, will be to boost the rocket into orbit piece by piece and assemble it there.

To do so would require establishing a large permanent orbital space station, with living and sleeping quarters for the engineers and technicians who will put the space ship together and check out its systems and equipment. Only a few of those who must work aboard the station will be trained pilots and astronauts. Weightlessness may pose a severe problem for the others. Thus it probably will prove advisable to generate artificial gravity. This is done by constructing the station in the shape of a large wheel, perhaps several hundred feet in diameter. Centrifugal force will create the sensation of gravity. "Down" will seem to be toward the rim of the wheel.

Assembling the huge space ship in orbit will be difficult for the workmen, who will have to wear space suits and be careful of the sun. One part of the job might be easier than on earth, however. Some welding jobs must be done on earth in a closed space from which all the air has been removed. The usual practice is to replace the air with a chemically inert gas, such as helium, neon or argon. Air must be removed to prevent the metal from burning in the intense heat of the welding arc. But welding can be done in the open in the vacuum of space.

The interplanetary spacecraft can also be assembled at a space station in orbit about the moon, or on the moon itself. In both cases, the total expenditure of fuel would be greater, because rocket propulsion would be needed first to back into the moon's gravitational field and then to escape it. There might be advantages, however. The energy required for the trip to Venus or Mars would be less from lunar orbit than earth orbit; thus the fuel tanks for the interplanetary portion of the journey could be smaller, reducing the over-all size of the spacecraft itself. The operation would become economical if a substantial portion of the fuel could be obtained on the moon.

For assembly on the moon itself, almost all of the fuel would have to be obtained there. Even so, this would be a very expensive operation, because fuel would have to be expended in great quantities to deliver the parts to the moon. However, it would simplify somewhat the problems of the workmen. They would still have to wear space suits and protect themselves from the sun, but would have the convenience of working in gravity conditions—yet a low gravity in which heavy objects could be moved easily.

In the more distant future, probably after the turn of the century, men will explore the more distant planets. Mercury, nearest to the sun, may provide a platform for solar observation instruments. In the opposite direction, just beyond Mars, is Jupiter, the largest of the planets, source of powerful radio waves, with a somewhat insubstantial surface and an unexplained great red spot. Next is Saturn, with its famous rings. And after Saturn are the very cold planets, Uranus, Neptune and Pluto.

For planets more distant than Venus and Mars, the propulsion requirements and the travel time rise steadily. Here is a table that shows what change in speed is necessary for an object starting from an orbit 400 miles above the earth, if it is to follow a coasting path of minimum energy, along an ellipse that touches the orbit of the earth at the beginning and the orbit of the target planet at its destination. Another column tells the one-way travel time.

Planet	Velocity Change (miles per second)	Travel Time
Mercury	3.42	106 days
Venus	2.13	146 days
Mars	2.19	259 days
Jupiter	3.90	33 months
Saturn	4.50	6 years
Uranus	5.00	16 years
Neptune	5.14	31 years
Pluto	5.20	46 years

It is clear that the propulsion requirement climbs slowly for trips to the distant planets, although the travel time becomes enormous. A speed of about five miles per second is necessary to launch a satellite into orbit about the earth. If we add another five miles a second to the speed and point it in the right direction, the satellite eventually will reach Neptune or Pluto. But minimum energy travel will obviously take too long. Manned flights to the distant planets will require new forms of propulsion, which will make it possible to expend much greater amounts of energy and shorten the travel time accordingly. Otherwise, the explorers would have to spend the better part of a lifetime en route. Some shortening of the time is possible if large ion rockets, with high fuel economy, can be developed.

One energy source that suggests itself is the thermonuclear reaction of the hydrogen bomb. In the next two or three decades, physicists expect to develop means of conducting such a reaction under controlled conditions. A thermonuclear rocket, which would "burn" hydrogen, might produce enough thrust for trips to the far planets with very high fuel economy. The highest fuel economy of all would be achieved by a photon rocket, in which thrust would be the reaction force produced by an extremely bright light shining out of the rear of the vehicle. A law of rocket propulsion says fuel economy (properly called specific impulse) is proportional to the speed of the stream of particles shooting out the rocket nozzle. Thus if the particles leave at the speed of light, the mileage per gallon reaches its ultimate. However, such a rocket would not shine visible light. To attain high energy, and thus high thrust, the radiation would be very short wavelength X-rays of gamma rays. It will be a severe technical problem to find means of focusing such radiation, which penetrates solid matter and thus cannot use a solid mirror.

A combination of the thermonuclear reactor as a source of energy and the photon rocket as the operating drive may provide a high-thrust, low-fuel-consumption system of propulsion that will enable explorers of the next century to reach Uranus, Neptune and perhaps even Pluto. Such a trip will be a long one at best. Pluto never comes closer than three and a half billion miles from the earth; its light takes more than five hours to reach us, traveling 186,000 miles a second.

But the end of the solar system is just about the limit of the travel we can now foresee for men. The light from Alpha Centauri, the nearest star, takes more than four years to reach us; it is 6650 times farther from the sun than Pluto. Other stars are much farther than Alpha Centauri. The Milky Way, our galaxy of stars, is a disk so huge that light needs more than 100,000 years to travel from rim to opposite rim.

The other galaxies are yet more distant. Our nearest neighbor, a relatively small collection of stars, is the Large Magellanic Cluster, 85,000 light-years away. The nearest full-scale galaxy is M31, the great Andromeda spiral, whose light takes 750,000 years to reach us. Distances to other galaxies are measured in the millions of light-years. The most powerful telescopes now can detect galaxies whose light has taken more than a billion years to arrive. If there is an end to the universe, astronomers have not yet found evidence of it. In any case, it is a very large place.

On the cosmic scale, flight to the moon is a small step. But it is a beginning. Men will want to go farther, if only to satisfy their desire for adventure and curiosity about the unknown. There will be continuing debate on the wisdom of spending so much money, on whether military or commercial values will accrue, on the scientific importance of the planets and on whether a nation's prestige requires planetary exploration. But the outcome of the debates is inevitable. When it becomes technically feasible, men will explore the planets, the stars and even the other galaxies. There are no limits to the possibilities; it is merely a matter of time. A million years from now, history will record A.D. 1957 and 1961 as the dates when men's instruments and then men themselves first flew from the racial birthplace, the third planet in the system of Sol, an average star near the periphery of the Milky Way galaxy.

Unless human civilization destroys itself in a nuclear war.

APPENDICES

Present and Proposed U.S. Launching Rockets

VEHICLE	STAGES					Payload Capacity (pounds in orbit)	TYPICAL APPLICATIONS
	I	II	III	IV	V		
Scout	Algol-solid fuel 103,000 pounds thrust	Castor-solid fuel 62,000 pounds thrust	Antares, solid fuel 13,600 pounds thrust	Altair, solid fuel 2800 pounds thrust		150	Scientific satellite
Delta	Thor-Lox, Kerosene fuel 150,000 pounds thrust	Delta-nitric acid & Hydrazine fuel 7700 pounds thrust	Altair			500	Scientific, communication satellites
Thor-Agena B	Thor	Agena B-Nitric Acid & Hydrazine fuel, 15,000 pounds thrust				1,600	Scientific, military weather satellites
Atlas-Agena B	Atlas booster, two Lox-Kerosene engines, total thrust 300,000 pounds	Atlas sustainer, one Lox-Kerosene engine, 60,000 pounds thrust	Agena B			5,000	Scientific, military, satellites, deep space probes
Centaur	Atlas booster	Atlas sustainer	Centaur, two Lox-liquid hydrogen engines, total thrust 30,000 pounds			8,500	Scientific, weather, communication satellites deep space probes

Present and Proposed U.S. Launching Rockets (Continued)

VEHICLE	STAGES					Payload Capacity (pounds in orbit)	TYPICAL APPLICATIONS
	I	II	III	IV	V		
Saturn C-1	S-I, eight H-1 Lox-Kerosene engines, total thrust 1,500,000 pounds.	S-IV, Six Centaur engines, total thrust 90,000 pounds	(For some applications) S-V modified Centaur			20,000	Apollo earth orbit missions, Dyna-soar, deep space probes
Saturn C-2*	S-I	S-II, Four J-2 Lox-liquid hydrogen engines, total thrust 800,000 pounds.	S-IV	S-V for some missions		45,000	Operational manned military spacecraft, deep space probes
Saturn C-3* (Liquid)	S-IB, Two F-1 Lox-Kerosene engines, total thrust 3,000,000 pounds.	S-II (With longer tankage than on Saturn C-2).	S-IV	S-V for some missions		80,000	Apollo cir-cumlunar flights
Saturn C-3* (Solid)	Cluster of solid engines, total thrust 5,000,000 pounds.	Same as liquid	Same as liquid	Same as liquid		80,000	Apollo Cir-cumlunar flights
Saturn C-4* (Also called Nova 4) (Liquid)	Four F-1 engines, total thrust 6,000,000 pounds.	S-II (with longer tankage than on Saturn C-3)	S-IV-B, one J-2 engine, thrust 200,000 pounds	S-V for some missions		160,000	Apollo cir-cumlunar flights, rendezvous two payloads for lunar landing

Present and Proposed U.S. Launching Rockets (Continued)

VEHICLE	STAGES					Payload Capacity (pounds in orbit)	TYPICAL APPLICATIONS
	I	II	III	IV	V		
Advanced Saturn (Saturn C-5) (Liquid)‡	S-I B, Five F-1 engines, total thrust 7,500,000 pounds	S-II, Five J-Z engines, total thrust 1,000,000 pounds	S-IV B	S-V for some missions		200,000	Apollo circumlunar flights, rendezvous two payloads for lunar landing
Advanced Saturn (Nuclear)*	S-I B	S-II	Nuclear Nerva (thrust classified)	Lunar landing stage	Lunar takeoff stage	350,000	Apollo lunar landing
Nova (Liquid)	N-I, Eight F-1 engines, total thrust 12,000,000 pounds	N-II, Four M-1 engines, total thrust 4,800,000 pounds	N-III, similar to S-IV B, one J-Z	Lunar landing stage	Lunar takeoff stage	350,000	Apollo lunar landing
Nova (Solid)*	Cluster of solid engines, total thrust 20,000,000 pounds	Same as liquid	Same as liquid	Lunar landing stage	Lunar takeoff stage	350,000	Apollo lunar landing

* Proposed
‡ Version with solid first stage has also been proposed

U. S. Scientific Satellite and Deep-Space Probe Projects

PROJECT	TRAJECTORY	MISSION	LAUNCH VEHICLE	STATUS
Explorer	Earth orbits	Various scientific measurements	Various	Phasing out
Ranger	Earth-moon	Rough landing of survivable instruments	Atlas-Agena B	Seven flights beginning 1962
Mariner	To Venus and Mars vicinity	Measurements in interplanetary space and near planets	Atlas-Agena B (later Centaur)	First flight to Venus August, 1962
Surveyor	Earth-moon	Soft landing of TV transmitters and instruments	Centaur	First flights about 1963
Orbiting Solar Observatory	Earth orbit, about 350 miles	Continuous watch on solar activity	Delta	First flight 1962
Orbiting Geophysical Observatory	I—polar earth orbit; II—elliptical earth orbit	"Streetcar" satellite to carry many scientific experiments	I—Thor Agena B; II—Atlas-Agena B	First flight 1963
Orbiting Astronomical Observatory	Earth orbit, 500 miles	Observe stars with large telescope and other instruments	Atlas-Agena B	First flight late 1963 or 1964
Prospector	Earth-moon	Land large payload with roving vehicle, instruments and advance supplies for manned flight	Saturn	Flights begin about 1966
Voyager	Venus and Mars	Orbit planet and eject capsule for entry into planetary atmosphere	Saturn	Flights late 1960s

U. S. Military Satellites

PROJECT & SPONSOR	DESCRIPTION	LAUNCH VEHICLE	ORBIT	STATUS
Advent—Army	Instantaneous repeater Communication satellite	Centaur	24-hour equatorial	Low orbit tests begin 1962; full system test 1963 or 1964
ANNA—Army, Navy, Air Force, NASA	Geodetic satellite			
ARENTS—ARPA	Test satellite	Centaur	24-hour inclined	Flight tests 1962-63
Bambi—ARPA	Anti-ICBM satellite			
Discoverer—Air Force	System for tests of stabilization, re-entry and recovery techniques	Thor-Agena	Low polar	Flights 1959—?
Dyna-Soar—Air Force, NASA	Manned space glider to test controlled re-entry	Titan III	Low, inclined	Flight tests 1964
Midas—Air Force	Warns of missile launchings by detecting infrared from rocket exhaust	Atlas-Agena	2000-mile	Flight tests 1960—?
SAINT—Air Force	Inspects possibly hostile after achieving near-rendez-vous	Atlas-Agena	Same as target	Flight tests soon
SAMOS—Air Force	Reconnaissance satellite	Atlas-Agena	Low polar	Flight tests 1961—?
Transit—Navy	Navigation satellite	Thor-Able Star, Scout later	Low inclined	Flight tests 1960-62 Operational 1962

U.S. Communication Satellites and Related Experiments

PROJECT & SPONSOR	SPACECRAFT*	LAUNCH VEHICLE	TRAJECTORY	LAUNCH DATE OR EXPECTED DATE	REMARKS
SCORE (ARPA–Army)	Atlas plus 150 pounds communication equipment	Atlas	Orbit, 110–910 miles	December 18, 1958	Operated twelve days; transmitted human voice (President Eisenhower's) from space for first time
Echo I (NASA)	Aluminum-coated plastic 100-foot balloon	Thor-Delta	Orbit, 945–1049 miles	August 12, 1960	Operated for more than a year but punctures caused loss of gas, surface wrinkles and thus poor quality signals
Courier I-B (Army)	500-pound delayed repeater, with 300 pounds equipment.	Thor-AbleStar	Orbit, 501–658 miles	October 4, 1960	Operated eighteen days
Explorer XII (NASA)	83-pound radiation experiment package	Thor-Delta	Elliptical orbit	August 15, 1961	Will provide detailed information on radiation belts needed to predict life of electronic components
Echo II (NASA)	Rigidized aluminum-coated plastic 135-foot balloon	Thor	Suborbital to 700-800 miles altitude & 600 miles downrange	1962	Two firings planned to test inflation
Echo II (NASA)	Same	Thor-Agena B	Orbit, 700 miles	1962	Other agencies plan communication experiments

U.S. Communication Satellites and Related Experiments (Continued)

PROJECT & SPONSOR	SPACECRAFT*	LAUNCH VEHICLE	TRAJECTORY	LAUNCH DATE OR EXPECTED DATE	REMARKS
Telstar (AT&T)	125-pound active repeater, sphere shape	Thor-Delta	Orbit, 600-3000 miles	1962	Two to four firings planned; broad-band transmission will carry voice, telegraph and TV
SynCom (NASA)	50-pound active repeater	Thor-Delta plus small solid fourth stage	22,300-mile (24-hour) 33° inclined orbit	Late 1962	Narrow-band transmission; no TV
Relay (NASA)	100-pound active repeater, octagon shape	Thor-Delta	Orbit, 1000-3000 miles	1962	Two firings planned; broad band transmission capacity including TV
ARENTS (ARPA)	Test Satellite	Centaur	22,300-mile (24-hour) inclined orbit	1962-63	Three firings planned; will carry "piggyback" similar to Explorer XII
Relay-Advanced (NASA)	Two or more Relays in one package	Atlas-Agena B	Orbit, 5000-6000 miles	1963	
Rebound (NASA)	Three Echo II balloons in one package	Atlas-Agena B	Orbit, 1500-2500 miles	1963	
Advent (Army)	Active Repeater	Centaur	22,300-mile (24-hour) equatorial orbit	1963	

*Weights subject to change

U. S. Weather Satellites—Research and Development

PROJECT	TIME PERIOD	WEIGHT (POUNDS)	INSTRUMENTATION	ORBIT	ORIENTATION	LAUNCH VEHICLE
Tiros I	1960	270	Two TV cameras	400-mile circular, 50° inclination	Spin-stabilized	Thor-Able
Tiros II-VI	1960-62	280	Two TV cameras, infrared sensors	400-mile circular, 50° inclination	Spin-stabilized	Delta
Nimbus	1962-64	600	multiple TV cameras, infrared sensors	600-mile circular, 80° inclination	Always points to earth	Thor-Agena
Advanced Nimbus	Mid 1960s	not set	TV cameras, infrared sensors, solar measurements, infrared spectrometer, radar	Not set	Always points to earth	Not set
Aeros	1964-65	600 or more	Zoomar camera, others not set	24-hour equatorial	Always points to earth	Centaur

All research and development weather satellite projects are under direction of the National Aeronautics and Space Administration.

U. S. Weather Satellite Plans—Operational

PHASE AND TIME PERIOD	LAUNCHINGS	SATELLITES IN ORBIT
I, July, 1962– December, 1963	Five Nimbus plus two backups	One Nimbus almost all of the time
II, January, 1964– December, 1965.	Six Nimbus plus two backups; two Aeros	One Nimbus at all times; a second most of the time; one Aeros part of the time
III, January, 1966, on	Three Nimbus and one backup annually; two Aeros annually	Two Nimbus at all times; one Aeros part of the time

All operational weather satellites are under control of the Weather Bureau. NASA will procure and launch them for the Weather Bureau. The operational satellite plans include some to be launched by NASA for research and development.

INDEX

Mercury, Project, 17, 24, 32, 76, 77, 79-82, 89, 94, 96-101, 113, 114, 116-18, 142, 143, 145, 192, 195, 201, 207-9, 212, 213, 224, 234, 240
Meridian House Foundation, 191
Meteorological Satellites, Panel on, 175
Mexican War, 39
Mexico, Gulf of, 32
Michigan, University of, 210
Michoud Ordnance Plant, 32
Midas, Project, 138
Milky Way galaxy, 250, 251
Miller, George P., 199
Minow, Newton N., 156-58
Minuteman missile, 180, 220
Mississippi Test Center, 32
Mitchell, Elliot, 8
Mittauer, Richard T., 9
MOUSE, 47, 50
Municipal Manpower Commission, 191
Muroc, Calif., 118
Myers, Boyd C., II, 77
Mysore, India, 38

NACA, see National Advisory Committee for Aeronautics
Nashville, Tenn., 210
National Academy of Sciences, 49, 50, 61, 73, 118, 126, 148
National Advisory Cancer Council, 192
National Advisory Committee for Aeronautics, 72-75, 206-9
National Aeronautic Association, 93, 94
National Aeronautics and Space Council, 6-8, 106, 160, 189, 195-97, 199, 201, 204
National Bureau of Standards, 209, 215
National Defense Research Committee, 43
National Science Foundation, 49, 50, 193
National Security Council, 50, 201
National Security Resources Board, 196
Naval Research Laboratory, 50, 51, 105, 206

Navy, U. S., 43-45, 47, 48, 50-52, 56, 59, 66, 79, 105, 140, 141, 179, 180, 207, 220
Nebel, Rudolf, 108
Nehru, Pandit Jawaharlal, 186
Neptune, planet, 249, 250
NERVA, Project, 223
Nesmeyanov, A. N., 48, 52
New Orleans, La., 32
Newell, Homer E., 8, 48, 125, 126, 212
Newlon, F. Clarke, 9
Newton, Sir Isaac, 37
Niedersachswerfen, Germany, 44
Nike-Zeus missile, 140
Nimbus, Project, 170-76
Norton Sound, U. S. S., 63
Nova, Project, 30, 31, 201, 214-18, 221, 228
Nuclear-electric rockets, see electric rockets
Nuclear rockets, 30, 197, 199, 202, 216, 217, 222, 223, 238, 239, 246, 247
Nunn, Robert G., Jr., 8, 152, 157

Oak Ridge Institute of Nuclear Studies, 192
Oberth, Hermann, 40, 41, 107
Oceanus Procellarum, 229
Odishaw, Hugh, 48, 72, 126
O'Keefe, J. A., 65
Oklahoma City, Okla., 192
Operations Coordinating Board, 73
Orbiter, Project, 47, 50
Orbiting Astronomical Observatory, 133, 236
Orbiting Geophysical Observatory, 134
Orion, Project, 237

Pacific Missile Range, 171
Palomar Observatory, 236
Paperclip, Operation, 44
Peenemuende, Germany, 42, 44, 85, 107, 111
Pendray, G. Edward, 41
Pershing, missile, 105
Phillips, Franklyn, 8
Phillips, Joseph, 9
Photon rocket, 250
Pioneer I, 67
Pioneer II, 68